#315

LAVAND SYVERSON
AMERICAN UNIVERSITY HOSPITAL
BEIRUT, LEBANON

From LaVand & Beverly Syverson (Cherry Valley. CA)
May 1994 on the occasion of their
40th Class reunion at Wheaton College
and they stayed with me.

MODERN QUARTETS
for MEN

Music Editors
B. D. ACKLEY and C. AUSTIN MILES

Compiled by
HOMER RODEHEAVER

Special Arrangements
by
NORMAN PRICE

Published by
The RODEHEAVER
HALL – MACK Co.
WINONA LAKE, INDIANA

Printed in U. S. A.

PREFACE

Due to paper restrictions this edition of MODERN QUARTETS FOR MEN is not printed on Eye Conditioned paper, as were previous editions. As soon as conditions permit we hope to return to printing on that paper.

To arrange music for men's voices is a task requiring a practical knowledge of those essentials which are desirable if success is to be assured.

From the many others well qualified to undertake such a work, Mr. Norman Price was selected, and nearly all of the songs have been arranged by him.

His experience as a Church soloist, a radio artist and especially as an arranger of vocal music on the staff of the N. B. C. has provided him the opportunity to learn the demands of both singer and listener; his ability as a musician is a guarantee that the work has been well done.

Many of the arrangements are unique. Some of the old songs, favorites for many years, are surprisingly refreshing in their treatment, musically, without needless violation of the rules of harmonic construction or the tenets of good taste.

We are hopeful that MODERN QUARTETS will merit the approval of every Quartet and Chorus of Men's Voices.

THE PUBLISHERS.

Modern Quartets

for

Men

BEYOND THE SUNSET

VIRGIL P. BROCK

BLANCHE KERR BROCK

1. Be-yond the sun-set, O bliss-ful morn-ing, When with our Sav-iour heav'n is be-gun. Earth's toil-ing end-ed, O glo-rious dawn-ing; Be-yond the sun-set, when day is done.

2. Be-yond the sun-set no clouds will gath-er, No storms will threat-en, no fears an-noy; O day of glad-ness, O day un-end-ing, Be-yond the sun-set, e-ter-nal joy!

3. Be-yond the sun-set a hand will guide me To God, the Fa-ther, whom I a-dore; His glo-rious pres-ence, His words of wel-come, Will be my por-tion on that fair shore.

4. Be-yond the sun-set, O glad re-un-ion, With our dear loved ones who've gone be-fore; In that fair home-land we'll know no part-ing, Be-yond the sun-set for ev-er-more!

2 JESUS IS WITH ME

A. H. ACKLEY

B. D. ACKLEY

1. How do I know that my Lord is di - vine? His gra-cious presence is
2. What does it mat - ter tho' I am be - reft? Robbed of all things un- til
3. Why should I doubt what lies o - ver the hill? Je - sus has prom-ised my

con - stant - ly mine, Noth - ing can change Him what - ev - er I do,
noth - ing is left, Noth - ing but Je - sus? if Je - sus stands by,
hope to ful - fil, What is that hope? to be a - ble to say,

CHORUS

His love a - bides and for - ev - er is true.
Nothing else mat - ters in earth, sea or sky. } Je - sus is with me.
"Je - sus is mine," at the close of life's day.

won-der-ful joy, Noth- ing but sin can our friendship de-stroy; His grace will

keep me hap - py and free, Noth-ing shall come between Je - sus and me.

3 IN THEE DO I LIVE

C. A. M.   C. Austin Miles

1. All that I am or hope to be, O Son of God, I owe to Thee,
2. Thy blessed cross has sealed my peace, Thy sorrows make my own to cease;
3. Thy cruel wounds my own have healed; Thy brok-en heart my par-don sealed;

For Thou has bought me; I am Thine, And by Thy mer-cy Thou art mine.
Thy pow'r has cleansed me from all sin, Thy presence keeps my conscience clean.
Thy death, O Christ, means life for me, A life for all e-ter-ni-ty.

CHORUS

Thy mer-cy sought me, Thy love has bought me, Thy grace has

taught me to be-lieve. Then, in be-liev-ing, Thy peace re-

ceiv-ing, Now in Thee on-ly, do I live......

4 KEEP ON PRAYING

I. P. W.

INA PEARLE WHALEY

1. Keep on pray-ing when the skies are gray, In God's presence clouds will
2. Keep on pray-ing when the path grows dim, He will guide you if you
3. Keep on pray-ing for the soul a-stray Lost in dark-ness, far from
4. Keep on pray-ing, prayer is not in vain, Day by day new vic-t'ries

break a-way; Keep on pray-ing till the sun shines thro', For
look to Him; Light from heav-en He will sure-ly send, For
Love's bright way, Ask for help the wand'ring one to win, For
you will gain; More like Je-sus you will ev-er grow, For

CHORUS

God an-swers prayer. Keep on pray-ing, God is ev-er near;

Keep on pray-ing, He will sure-ly hear, (If you will,) Keep on pray-ing,

keep on trust-ing, too, Keep on pray-ing, God will an-swer you.

YOU MUST OPEN THE DOOR

INA DULEY OGDON   HOMER RODEHEAVER

1. There's a Sav-iour, who stands at the door of your heart, He is
2. He has come from the Fa-ther sal-va-tion to bring, And His
3. He is lov-ing and kind, full of in-fi-nite grace, In your
4. He will lead you at last to that bless-ed a-bode, To the

long-ing to en-ter—why let Him de-part? He has pa-tient-ly
name is called Je-sus, Re-deem-er and King; To save you and
heart, in your life, will you give Him a place? He is wait-ing to
cit-y of God, at the end of the road, Where the night never

called you so oft-en be-fore, But you must o-pen the door.
keep you He pleads ev-er-more, But you must o-pen the door.
bless you your soul to re-store, But you must o-pen the door.
falls, when life's jour-ney is o'er, But you must o-pen the door.

CHORUS

You must o-pen the door, You must o-pen the door, When

Je-sus comes in, He will save you from sin, But you must o-pen the door.

LIS'NING AT THE HEART'S DOOR

A. H. ACKLEY

B. D. ACKLEY

BARITONE AND TENOR DUET

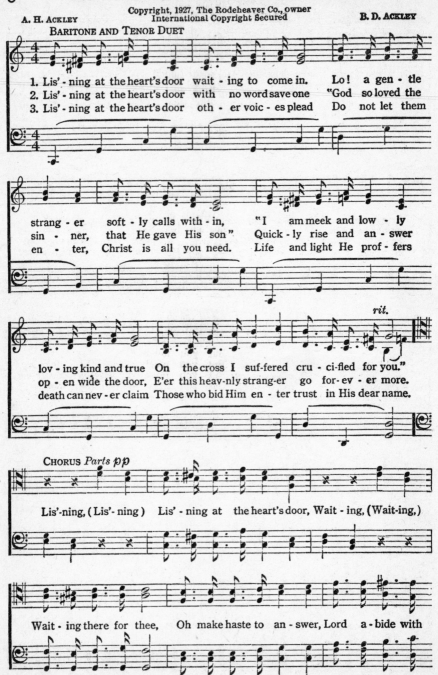

1. Lis' - ning at the heart's door   wait - ing to   come in.   Lo!   a gen - tle
2. Lis' - ning at the heart's door   with   no word save one   "God   so loved the
3. Lis' - ning at the heart's door   oth - er voic - es plead   Do   not let them

strang - er   soft - ly calls with - in,   "I   am meek and low - ly
sin - ner,   that He gave His son"   Quick - ly rise and an - swer
en - ter,   Christ is all   you need.   Life   and light He prof - fers

lov - ing kind and true   On   the cross I suf - fered cru - ci - fied for you."
op - en wide the door,   E'er this heav-nly strang-er   go   for - ev - er more.
death can nev - er claim   Those who bid Him en - ter trust   in His dear name.

CHORUS *Parts* pp

Lis'-ning, (Lis'-ning)   Lis' - ning at   the heart's door,   Wait - ing, (Wait-ing,)

Wait - ing there for thee,   Oh make haste to   an - swer, Lord   a - bide with

LIS'NING AT THE HEART'S DOOR

me, Wait - ing at the heart's door, Wait - ing now for Thee.

7 LEAD ME TO CALVARY

JENNIE EVELYN HUSSEY

WM. J. KIRKPATRICK

1. King of my life, I crown Thee now, Thine shall the glo - ry be;
2. Show me the tomb where Thou wast laid, Ten - der - ly mourned and wept;
3. Let me like Ma - ry, thro' the gloom, Come with a gift to Thee;
4. May I be will - ing, Lord, to bear Dai - ly my cross for Thee;

Lest I for - get Thy thorn-crowned brow, Lead me to Cal - va - ry.
An - gels in robes of light ar - rayed Guard-ed Thee whilst Thou slept.
Show to me now the emp - ty tomb, Lead me to Cal - va - ry.
E - ven Thy cup of grief to share, Thou hast borne all for me.

CHORUS

Lest I for-get Geth-sem - a - ne; Lest I for-get Thine ag - o - ny;

Lest I for - get Thy love for me, Lead me to Cal - va - ry.

8 GOOD NIGHT AND GOOD MORNING

LIZZIE DEARMOND · HOMER RODEHEAVER

1. When comes to the weary a bless-ed re-lease, When up-ward we pass to His
2. When home-lights we see shining brightly a-bove, Where we shall be soon thro' His
3. When fadeth the day and dark shadows draw nigh, With Christ close at hand it is

King-dom of peace, When free from the woes that on earth we must bear, We'll
won-der-ful love, We'll praise Him who called us His Heav-en to share, We'll
not death to die; He'll wipe ev-'ry tear, roll a-way ev-'ry care; We'll

CHORUS

say, "good-night" here, but "goodmorning" up there. Goodmorning up there where

Christ is the light, Goodmorning up there, where cometh no night; When we step from this

earth, to God's heaven so fair, we'll say goodnight here, But goodmorning up there.

9 SOMEBODY KNOWS

ALFRED H. ACKLEY

B. D. ACKLEY

1. Fail-ing in strength when op-prest by my foes, Some-bod-y knows,
2. Wounded and help-less and sick with dis-tress, Some-bod-y knows,
3. Why should I fear when the care-bil-lows roll? Some-bod-y knows,

Some-bod-y knows; Wait-ing for some one to ban-ish my woes,
Some-bod-y knows; Long-ing for home and a moth-er's ca-ress,
Some-bod-y knows; When the deep shad-ows sweep o-ver my soul,

Some-bod-y knows, 'Tis Je-sus. Some-bod-y knows,

CHORUS

Some-bod-y knows When I am temp-ted and tried by my foes;

He is the one who will keep me— Some-bod-y knows, 'Tis Je-sus.

10   A SHARE IN THE ATONEMENT

C. A. M.   C. AUSTIN MILES

1. At one with God, how rich is my con-di-tion; At peace with Him where
2. Condemned was He, but I received a pardon. A sin-ner, I. The
3. He bore the cross, but I received a blessing. All that I have or

ev-er I may be. Be-tween us, then, all bar-ri-ers were broken When
sin-less One was He, To ran-som me, the Son of God was will-ing To
am, or hope to be,— This do I owe, nor can I e'er re-pay Him Who

Je-sus made a-tonement on Cal-va-ry.
make a full a-tonement on Cal-va-ry.
made complete a-tonement on Cal-va-ry.

CHORUS

I have a share in that a-tone-ment Which was made on Cal-va-ry. What a treas-ure is mine, This gift so di-vine, That no one can take a-way from me.

WONDERFUL

A. H. A.

A. H. ACKLEY

1. Won-der - ful birth, to a man-ger He came, Made in the like-ness of
2. Won-der - ful life, full of serv-ice so free, Friend to the poor and the
3. Won-der - ful death, for it meant not de - feat, Cal - va - ry made His great
4. Won-der - ful hope, He is com-ing a - gain, Com - ing as King o'er the

man to pro - claim God's boundless love for a world sick with sin, Pleading with
need- y was He; Un - fail - ing goodness on all He bestowed, Un - dy- ing
mis- sion com - plete, Wrought our redemption, and when He a - rose, Ban-ished for-
na - tions to reign; Glo - ri - ous promise, His word can-not fail, His righteous

CHORUS

sin-ners to let Him come in.
faith in the vil - est He showed.
ev - er the last of our foes.
kingdom at last must pre - vail!

Wonder- ful name He bears, Won-der- ful

crown He wears, Wonder - ful blessings His triumphs af - ford; Won - der- ful

Cal - va -ry, Wonder- ful grace for me, Wonder - ful love of my Wonder - ful Lord!

SUMMER ALL THE TIME

A. H. A.   A. H. ACKLEY

1. Ros - es in De-cem - ber God has giv - en me, In the won-drous
2. Ros - es in De-cem - ber when the days are drear, When the chill - ing
3. Ros - es in De-cem - ber God will give to you, List - en while the

Hum

bless - ings of His love; Sweet-er far than an - y flow'rs of
winds of sor - row blow, God pro-vides the tok - ens of His
se - cret I im - part: When you know the Sav - iour, you will

earth could be, Are the ones He sends me from a - bove........
grace to cheer, Just be-cause He loves His chil - dren so...........
find them, too, Grow-ing in the gar-den of your heart......

CHORUS

Ros - es in De-cem - ber, song-birds in the night, Since the lov - ing

Sav - iour filled my heart with light, His a - bid - ing pres - ence

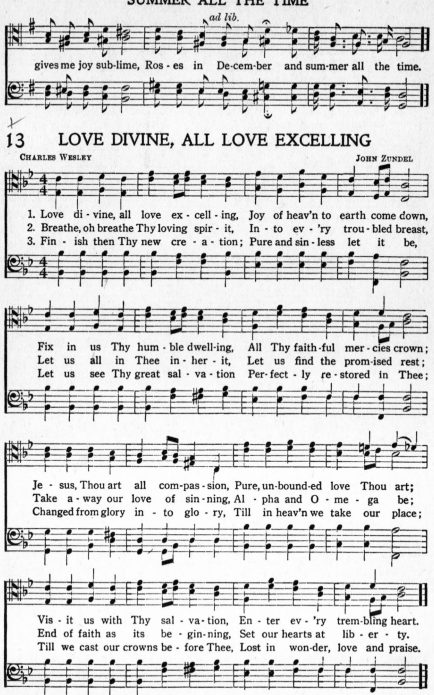

14 WE SHALL ALWAYS BE HAPPY OVER THERE

A. H. ACKLEY   B. D. ACKLEY

1. No more burdens, no more heartaches no more sor-row, No more grieving
2. No more la - bor thro' the days so long and wea - ry, No more longings
3. No more hap-py hours to end and leave us lone - ly, No more in - ter
4. No more death to fill the soul with fear and trembling, No more sad-ness

o'er the bro-ken things of life; Not a cloud to mar the sky of God's to-
un - ful-filled, no friends untrue; No more journeys thro' the shadowed vale so
rupt - ed sea-sons of de-light; Fade-less pleasures we shall find in heav-en
when our dear ones say "Good-by;" Ev - 'ry joy love can pro-vide God is as-

mor - row, Not a foe to curse that bless - ed land with strife.
drear - y, With un - fet - tered spir - it we shall live a - new.
on - ly; Sweeter far than an - y dream of glo - ry bright.
sem - bling, In that par - a - dise with Christ be - yond the sky.

CHORUS

We shall al - ways be hap-py ov - er there For no e - vil can in-

vade that realm so fair; .... And the tears that blind our eyes

that realm so fair;

WE SHALL ALWAYS BE HAPPY OVER THERE

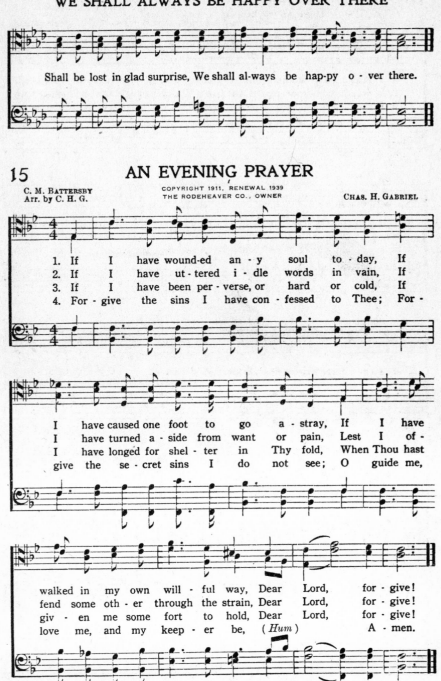

Shall be lost in glad surprise, We shall al-ways be hap-py o - ver there.

15   AN EVENING PRAYER

C. M. Battersby
Arr. by C. H. G.

CHAS. H. GABRIEL

1. If   I   have wound-ed   an - y   soul   to - day,   If
2. If   I   have ut - tered i - dle   words   in   vain,   If
3. If   I   have been per - verse, or   hard   or   cold,   If
4. For - give   the   sins I   have con - fessed   to Thee;   For -

I   have caused one foot   to   go   a - stray,   If   I have
I   have turned a - side from want   or   pain,   Lest   I   of -
I   have longed for shel - ter   in   Thy   fold,   When Thou hast
give   the   se - cret sins   I   do   not   see;   O   guide me,

walked   in   my   own   will - ful   way,   Dear   Lord,   for - give!
fend   some oth - er   through the strain, Dear   Lord,   for - give!
giv - en   me some   fort   to   hold, Dear   Lord,   for - give!
love   me,   and my   keep - er   be,   (*Hum*)   A - men.

A NEW NAME IN GLORY

C. A. M.

C. Austin Miles

1. I was once a sin-ner, but I came Par-don to re-ceive from my Lord.
2. I was humbly kneeling at the Cross Fearing naught but God's angry frown.
3. In the Book 'tis written "Sav'd by Grace," O the joy that came to my soul.

This was free-ly giv-en, and I found That He al-ways kept His word,
When the heavens o-pened and I saw That my name was writ-ten down.
Now I am for-giv-en and I know By the blood I am made whole.

CHORUS

There's a new name written down in glory, And it's mine, O yes it's mine!......
And it's mine, yes it's mine!

And the white robed angels sing the story, "A sin-ner has come home,"......
has come home,

For there's a new name written down in Glory, And it's mine, O yes, it's mine,......
And it's mine, yes, it's mine,

A NEW NAME IN GLORY

With my sins for-giv-en I am bound for heav-en, Nev-er-more to roam.

17

I LOVE HIM

London Hymn Book

S. C. FOSTER

Hum

1. Gone from my heart, the world with all its charm; Gone are the sins and
2. Once I was lost up-on the plain of sin; Once was a slave to
3. Once I was bound, but now I am set free; Once I was blind, but

Hum

Parts

all that would a-larm; Gone ev-er-more and by His grace I know The
doubts and fears with-in; Once was a-fraid to trust a liv-ing God, But
now the light I see; Once I was dead but now in Christ I live, To

CHORUS *pp*

precious blood of Je-sus cleanses white as snow.
now my guilt is washed away in Je-sus' blood. } I love Him, I love Him, Be-
tell the world the peace that He alone can give.

cause He first loved me, *Hum............* On Cal-va-ry.

And pur-chased my sal-va-tion on Cal-va-ry.

18 ONLY A TOUCH

IDA L. REED

B. D. ACKLEY

1. On - ly a touch of Thy hand, dear Lord, On - ly a word from
2. On - ly a touch of Thy hand, dear Lord, On - ly a word from
3. On - ly a touch of Thy hand, dear Lord, On - ly a word of

Thee, Will all my heart's wild an - guish still, Joy - ful my
Thee, Calms all my wea - ry, trou - bled soul, Still - eth life's
love, Will all my wounds and sor - rows heal, Lead me to

REFRAIN

soul shall be............
surg - ing sea............ On - ly a touch of Thy hand, dear Lord,
heav'n a - bove,........

And o'er my soul shall sweep, Mel - o - dy sweet from life's

bro - ken chords, A - wak - ened from si - - lence deep.

BLESSED HOUR OF PRAYER

FANNY CROSBY

W. H. DOANE

1. 'Tis the bless-ed hour of pray'r, when our hearts low-ly bend, And we gath-er to Je-sus, our Sav-iour and friend; If we come to Him in faith, His pro-tec-tion to share, What a balm for the wear-y! O how sweet to be there!

2. 'Tis the bless-ed hour of pray'r, when the Sav-iour draws near, With a ten-der com-pas-sion His chil-dren to hear; When He tells us we may cast at His feet ev-'ry care, What a balm for the wear-y! O how sweet to be there!

3. 'Tis the bless-ed hour of pray'r, when the tempt-ed and tried, To the Sav-iour who loves them their sor-rows con-fide; With a sym-pa-thiz-ing heart He removes ev-'ry care; What a balm for the wear-y! O how sweet to be there!

4. 'Tis the bless-ed hour of pray'r, trust-ing Him we be-lieve, That the bless-ings we're need-ing we'll sure-ly re-ceive, In the full-ness of this trust we shall lose ev-'ry care; What a balm for the wear-y! O how sweet to be there!

CHORUS

Bless-ed hour of pray'r, Bless-ed hour of pray'r, What a balm for the wear-y! O how sweet to be there!

20 THERE'S A RAINBOW SHINING SOMEWHERE

ANNE CAMPBELL

B. D. ACKLEY

1. When the cares of life as-sail me, Then I search the skies a-bove;
2. When the dark-ness falls a-round me, When the clouds a-bove my door
3. God will come to heal my sor-row, God will come to bring me peace,

For the God who will not fail me Sends an em-blem of His love.
Come to say that trou-ble's found me, Then I wacth the skies once more,
With a rain-bow on the mor-row, When the storms of life shall cease.

CHORUS

There's a rain-bow shin-ing somewhere, There's a light a-cross the skies;

There's a rain-bow shin-ing somewhere, Like a gleam from Par-a-dise;

Though to-day the clouds are drift-ing Far a-cross the storm-y sea,

THERE'S A RAINBOW SHINING SOMEWHERE

There's a rain-bow shin-ing somewhere That will some day shine for me.

HAVE YE BEEN TO NAZARETH?

21

COPYRIGHT 1921, RENEWAL 1949
THE RODEHEAVER CO., OWNER
INTERNATIONAL COPYRIGHT SECURED

GRACE GORDON   CLYDE WILLARD

1. Have ye been to Na-zareth, Low-ly, yet so fair? Yes, we sought His humble town,
2. Did ye find at Na-zareth, Christ the Son of God? Yea, He was the Son of Man,
3. Is there light from Nazareth, Dai-ly life to crown? Yes, the glo-ry streams a-far,

Found our Mas-ter there! Did He dwell in pal-ace fair, Hold-ing king-ly sway?
Earth-ly paths He trod. Did ye find a bless-ing there Ev-er to a-bide?
Dis-tant years a-down. Will the Lord of Na-zareth, Friend and Comrade be?

CHORUS

Nay, we found a Car-penter, Toil-ing day by day!)
Yea, by Him the toilsome tasks, E'er are glo-ri-fied. } In life's Na-za-reth we seek,
All unseen He dwells with us, As in Gal-i-lee!)

Christ, the Mas-ter, meek, In our toil from day to day, Find our Lord for aye!

HE'S ABLE AND WILLING

C. A. M.

C. Austin Miles

1. A sinner more wretched than I,......There could not be; 'Till Jesus the
2. His power no limit can know, His grace is mine; His love He is
3. He's able and willing to go,......O'er mountains steep, Or down in the

mighty, came nigh, To set me free, I opened my heart to His call,
willing to show, 'Tis love divine! His mercy is offered today,
valley so low, Or stormy deep: If willing His bidding to do,

His own to be, And when I surrendered all,...... My Lord saved me.
So full, so free, He'll never turn you away,..... For He saved me.
His own you'll be, I know He can keep you true..... For He keeps me.

REFRAIN

He's able and willing to save, Able......... willing,.........
Able and willing, able and willing,

He's able and willing to save, For He saved me.

23 A SINNER MADE WHOLE

W. M. LIGHTHALL   CHAS. H. GABRIEL

1. There's a song in my heart that my lips can-not sing, 'Tis praise in the
2. I shall stand one day fault-less and pure by His throne, Transformed from my
3. All the mu-sic of heav-en, so per-fect and sweet, Will blend with my

high-est to Je-sus my King; Its mu-sic each mo-ment is
im-age con-formed to His own; Then I shall find words for the
song just to make it com-plete; Thro' a-ges un-end-ing the

D.S.—*heart now is sing-ing there's*

FINE

thrill-ing my soul, For I was a sin-ner but Christ made me whole.
song of my soul, For I was a sin-ner but Christ made me whole.
ech-oes will roll, For I was a sin-ner but Christ made me whole.

joy in my soul, For I was a sin-ner but Christ made me whole.

CHORUS

A sin-ner made whole! A sin-ner made whole! The

D.C. al Fine

Sav-iour has bought me, and ran-somed my soul! My

SAVED BY GRACE

FANNY J. CROSBY   GEO. C. STEBBINS

1. Some day the sil - ver cord will break, And I no more as now shall sing;
2. Some day my earth - ly house will fall, I can-not tell how soon 'twill be,
3. Some day when fades the gold - en sun Be-neath the ros - y - tint - ed west,
4. Some day, till then I'll watch and wait, My lamp all trimmed and burning bright,

But, O the joy when I shall wake With-in the pal - ace of the King!
But this I know— my All in All Has now a place in heav'n for me.
My bless-ed Lord shall say, "well done!" And I shall en - ter in - to rest.
That when my Sav - iour ope's the gate, My soul to Him may take its flight.

CHORUS

And I shall see......... Him face to face,...... And tell the
shall see to face,

sto - ry, saved by grace, And I shall see......... Him face to
shall see

face, And tell the sto - ry, Saved by grace.
to face,

25 JESUS TOOK MY BURDEN

Rev. Johnson Oatman, Jr.　　　　　　　　　　　Bertha Mae Lillenas

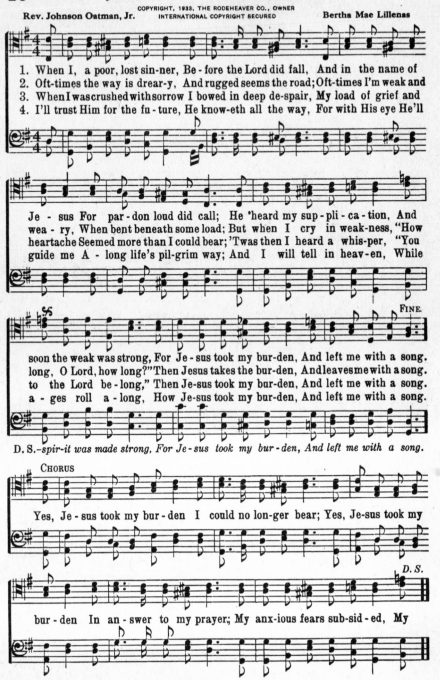

1. When I, a poor, lost sin-ner, Be-fore the Lord did fall, And in the name of
2. Oft-times the way is drear-y, And rugged seems the road; Oft-times I'm weak and
3. When I was crushed with sorrow I bowed in deep de-spair, My load of grief and
4. I'll trust Him for the fu-ture, He know-eth all the way, For with His eye He'll

Je - sus For par-don loud did call; He 'heard my sup-pli-ca-tion, And
wea - ry, When bent beneath some load; But when I cry in weak-ness, "How
heartache Seemed more than I could bear; 'Twas then I heard a whis-per, "You
guide me A - long life's pil-grim way; And I will tell in heav-en, While

soon the weak was strong, For Je-sus took my bur-den, And left me with a song.
long, O Lord, how long?" Then Jesus takes the bur-den, And leaves me with a song.
to the Lord be-long," Then Je-sus took my bur-den, And left me with a song.
a - ges roll a-long, How Je-sus took my bur-den, And left me with a song.

D. S.—*spir-it was made strong, For Je-sus took my bur-den, And left me with a song.*

CHORUS

Yes, Je-sus took my bur-den I could no lon-ger bear; Yes, Je-sus took my

D. S.

bur-den In an-swer to my prayer; My anx-ious fears sub-sid-ed, My

26 TILL THE MORNING

Carlton C. Buck

B. D. Ackley

1. Wea-ry soul, thou shalt rest in the morn-ing; Thou shalt lin-ger with the
2. Ev-'ry tear shall be dried in the morn-ing; I shall stand by Je-sus'
3. With the dawn of God's day in the morn-ing; Cares of night shall pass a-

blest in the morn-ing; Look-ing now be-yond life's task, Anx-ious
side in the morn-ing; Nev-er then to doubt nor fear, While my
way, in that morn-ing; With the thought of yon-der shore Comes the

Hum

hearts are sure to ask, "Will it be so ver-y long till the morn-ing?"
soul keeps ask-ing here, "Will it be so ver-y long till the morn-ing?"
ques-tion o'er and o'er, "Will it be so ver-y long till the morn-ing?"

Hum

Hum

CHORUS

In the morn-ing, in the morn-ing, It will not be ver-y

long till the morn-ing; With life's bur-den then laid down We'll re-

ceive the prom-ised crown; It will not be ver-y long till the morn-ing.

27 GOD IS WAITING IN THE SILENCE

Oswald J. Smith, D. D. B. D. Ackley

1. God is wait-ing in the si-lence For a heart that He can fill;
2. God is wait-ing in the si-lence,'Mid the rush and roar of life;
3. God is wait-ing in the si-lence As the world goes rush-ing by;

He must find it cleansed and emp-ty, With a spir-it calm and still.
Wait-ing,some-one's heart to en-ter, Some-one qui-et in the strife.
Will not some-one stop and lis-ten, An-swer quick-ly,"Here am I"?

CHORUS

God is wait-ing in the si-lence,—Oh, to know that He is near!

Earth re-cedes, and heav-en o-pens, Wait-ing, God is here.

God is wait-ing, God is here.

RISE UP, O MEN OF GOD

WILLIAM P. MERRILL

LLOYDE G. STROUSE

1. Rise up, O men of God! Have done with lesser things; Give heart and
2. Rise up, O men of God! The church for you doth wait, Her strength un-

soul and mind and strength To serve the King of kings. Rise up, O men of
e - qual to her task: Rise up, and make her great! Lift high the cross of

God! His king-dom tar-ries long: Bring in the day of broth-er-hood
Christ! Tread where His feet have trod! As broth-ers of the Son of Man,

And end (and end) the night of wrong, ... Bring in the day of
Rise up, rise up,) O men of God .... As broth-ers of the

broth - er-hood And end the night of wrong.
Son of Man, Rise (Omit............................) up, O men of God!

CHRIST AROSE

R. L.

Robert Lowry

1. Low in the grave He lay— Je - sus, my Sav - iour! Wait-ing the
2. Vain - ly they watch His bed— Je - sus, my Sav - iour! Vain - ly they
3. Death can-not keep his prey— Je - sus, my Sav - iour! He tore the

CHORUS

com-ing day— Je - sus, my Lord!
seal the dead— Je - sus, my Lord!
bars a - way— Je - sus, my Lord! Up from the grave He a-rose,

He a-rose,

With a might-y tri-umph o'er His foes; . . . . He a - rose a
He a - rose;

Vic-tor from the dark do-main, And He lives for - ev - er with His saints to reign:

He a - rose! . . . . He a - rose! . . . . Hal-le - lu - jah! Christ a - rose!
He a - rose! He a-rose!

HE IS MINE

C. Austin Miles

J. Lincoln Hall

1. There is a Shep-herd who cares for His own, And He is mine;
2. Je - sus left heav-en my Sav-iour to be, And He is mine;
3. There is a Com-fort-er come from a - bove, He too is mine;

Unison or Solo

Noth-ing am I, He's a King on a throne, But He is mine;
I am not worth all He suf-fered for me, But He is mine;
Com-ing to me to re-veal Je-sus' love, And that is mine;

How He can love such a sin - ner as I, Tho' He is mine;
Tho' I'm not wor-thy He dwells in my heart, And He is mine;
Shep-herd and Sav-iour, and Com-fort-er, too, They all are mine;

I can-not fath-om tho' oft-en I try, But He is mine.
From Him I'll nev-er, no nev-er de-part, For He is mine.
That's why I know the old sto-ry is true, They are all mine.

CHORUS

He is mine, ... He is mine;

Tho' all un-wor-thy, I know He is mine, He is mine;

HE IS MINE

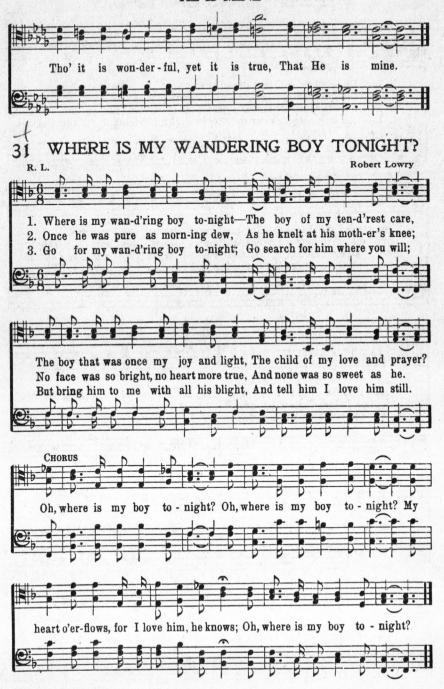

Tho' it is won-der-ful, yet it is true, That He is mine.

31 WHERE IS MY WANDERING BOY TONIGHT?

R. L.

Robert Lowry

1. Where is my wan-d'ring boy to-night—The boy of my ten-d'rest care,
2. Once he was pure as morn-ing dew, As he knelt at his moth-er's knee;
3. Go for my wan-d'ring boy to-night; Go search for him where you will;

The boy that was once my joy and light, The child of my love and prayer?
No face was so bright, no heart more true, And none was so sweet as he.
But bring him to me with all his blight, And tell him I love him still.

CHORUS

Oh, where is my boy to - night? Oh, where is my boy to - night? My

heart o'er-flows, for I love him, he knows; Oh, where is my boy to - night?

32 THE BREAKING OF THE DAY

Rev. Oswald J. Smith

COPYRIGHT, 1936. THE RODEHEAVER CO., OWNER
INTERNATIONAL COPYRIGHT SECURED

B. D. Ackley

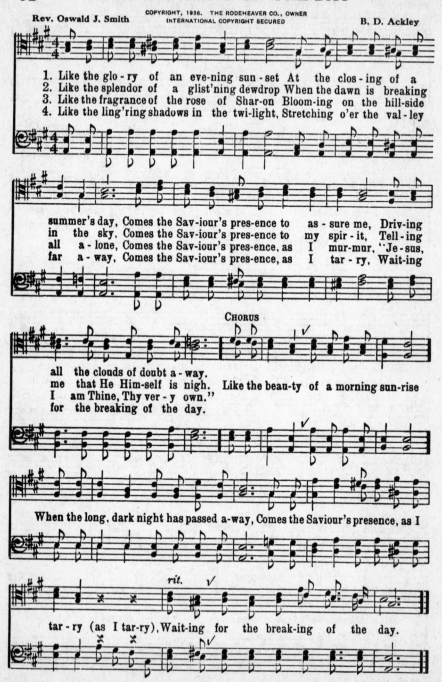

1. Like the glo-ry of an eve-ning sun-set At the clos-ing of a
2. Like the splendor of a glist'ning dewdrop When the dawn is breaking
3. Like the fragrance of the rose of Shar-on Bloom-ing on the hill-side
4. Like the ling'ring shadows in the twi-light, Stretching o'er the val-ley

summer's day, Comes the Sav-iour's pres-ence to as-sure me, Driv-ing
in the sky, Comes the Sav-iour's pres-ence to my spir-it, Tell-ing
all a-lone, Comes the Sav-iour's pres-ence, as I mur-mur, "Je-sus,
far a-way, Comes the Sav-iour's pres-ence, as I tar-ry, Wait-ing

CHORUS

all the clouds of doubt a-way.
me that He Him-self is nigh. Like the beau-ty of a morning sun-rise
I am Thine, Thy ver-y own."
for the breaking of the day.

When the long, dark night has passed a-way, Comes the Saviour's presence, as I

rit.

tar-ry (as I tar-ry), Wait-ing for the break-ing of the day.

FOR YOU I AM PRAYING

S. O'Malley Cluff

Ira D. Sankey

1. ✗ I have a Sav-iour, He's plead-ing in glo-ry, A
2. ✗ I have a Fa-ther; to me He has giv-en A
3. ✗ I have a robe, 'tis re-splen-dent in white-ness, A-
4. When Je-sus has found you, tell oth-ers the sto-ry, That

dear, lov-ing Sav-iour, though earth friends be few; And now He is
hope for e-ter-ni-ty, bless-ed and true; And soon He will
wait-ing in glo-ry my won-der-ing view; Oh, when I re-
my lov-ing Sav-iour is your Sav-iour too; Then pray that your

watch-ing in ten-der-ness o'er me, But oh, that my Sav-iour were
call me to meet Him in heav-en, But oh, that He'd let me bring
ceive it all shin-ing in brightness, Dear friend, could I see you re-
Sav-iour will bring them to glo-ry, And prayer will be an-swered, 'twas

CHORUS

your Sav-iour too!
you with me too! For you I am pray-ing, For you I am
ceiv-ing one too!
an-swered for you!

Hum   Hum

Hum   Hum

pray-ing, For you I am pray-ing, I'm pray-ing for you.

34 GOOD-NIGHT SONG

Chas. H. Gabriel

B. D. Ackley

Intro. (*Play in Treble Clef*)

1. Be with us, Lord, this
2. Be with us, Lord, be

part-ing hour, Let Thy wings our shelter be; O let the Pen - te-cos-tal pow'r Ev - er
with us still Thru the slumber hours of night; And if it be Thy ho - ly will, Bring us

keep us near to Thee. Good - night, good - night, Let not our part-ing
to the morn-ing light. Good-night, good-night,

prayer be vain; Oh, may Thy peace at-tend us, Thy love and care de-fend us, And

rit. e dim.

keep us till we meet a-gain; Good-night, good-night, . . . Good - night.
Good-night, good-night, good-night,

ppp

35 ON JORDAN'S STORMY BANKS

D. W. C. Huntington   T. C. O'Kane

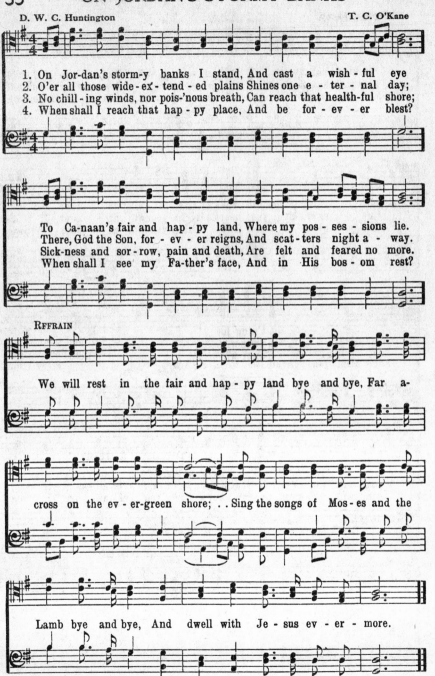

1. On Jor-dan's storm-y banks I stand, And cast a wish-ful eye
2. O'er all those wide-ex-tend-ed plains Shines one e-ter-nal day;
3. No chill-ing winds, nor pois-'nous breath, Can reach that health-ful shore;
4. When shall I reach that hap-py place, And be for-ev-er blest?

To Ca-naan's fair and hap-py land, Where my pos-ses-sions lie.
There, God the Son, for-ev-er reigns, And scat-ters night a-way.
Sick-ness and sor-row, pain and death, Are felt and feared no more.
When shall I see my Fa-ther's face, And in His bos-om rest?

REFRAIN

We will rest in the fair and hap-py land bye and bye, Far a-

cross on the ev-er-green shore; .. Sing the songs of Mos-es and the

Lamb bye and bye, And dwell with Je-sus ev-er-more.

I'LL BE SOMEWHERE, LIST'NING

Eduardo J. Lango

Eduardo J. Lango

1. When He calls me, I will an - swer, When He calls me, I will an - swer, When He calls me, I will an - swer, I'll be some-where, lis-t'ning for my name. I'll be some-where, lis-t'ning, I'll be some-where, lis-t'ning, I'll be some-where, lis-t'ning for my name. lis-t'ning for my name.

2. If your heart's right, you will an - swer, If your heart's right, you will an - swer, If your heart's right, you will an-swer when He calls. If your heart's right, you will an - swer, If your heart's right, you will an - swer, If your heart's right, you will an-swer when He calls. an-swer when He calls.

3. If you know Him, you will an - swer, If you know Him, you will an - swer, If you know Him, you will an-swer when He calls. If you know Him, you will an - swer, If you know Him, you will an - swer, If you know Him, you will an-swer when He calls. an-swer when He calls.

REFRAIN

SOFTLY AND TENDERLY

W. L. T.

Will L. Thompson

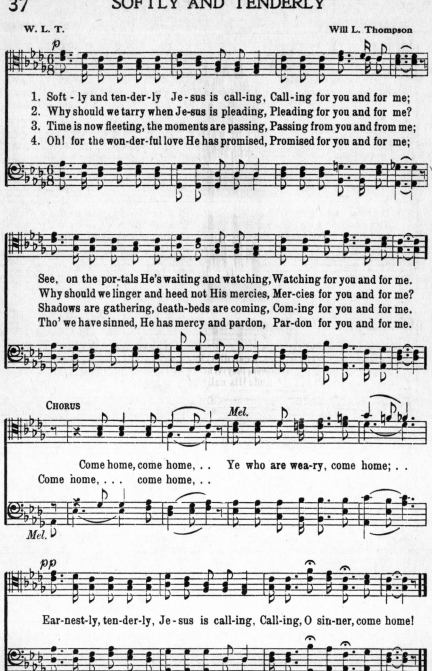

1. Soft - ly and ten-der-ly Je - sus is call-ing, Call-ing for you and for me;
2. Why should we tarry when Je-sus is pleading, Pleading for you and for me?
3. Time is now fleeting, the moments are passing, Passing from you and from me;
4. Oh! for the won-der-ful love He has promised, Promised for you and for me;

See, on the por-tals He's waiting and watching, Watching for you and for me.
Why should we linger and heed not His mercies, Mer-cies for you and for me?
Shadows are gathering, death-beds are coming, Com-ing for you and for me.
Tho' we have sinned, He has mercy and pardon, Par-don for you and for me.

CHORUS

Come home, come home, . . Ye who are wea-ry, come home; . .
Come home, . . . come home, . .

Ear-nest-ly, ten-der-ly, Je-sus is call-ing, Call-ing, O sin-ner, come home!

38 GALILEE

Elsie Duncan Yale

J. Lincoln Hall

1. O sun - lit ways (O sun - lit ways) Of Gal - i - lee (Of Gal - i - lee)!
2. O qui - et slope (O qui - et slope) Where once He taught (Where once He taught),
3. O peace-ful shore (O peace-ful shore) Of lake so fair (Of lake so fair),

O bless - ed days (O bless - ed days) Of mem - o - ry (Of mem - o - ry)!
The words of hope (The words of hope) To earth He bro't (To earth He bro't);
In days of yore (In days of yore) He lin-gered there (He lin-gered there),

No years can dim (No years can dim) The paths where trod (The paths where trod)
How blest were they (How blest were they) Whose hearts were stirred (Whose hearts were stirred),
Still sounds His call (Still sounds His call), Thru years to be (Thru years to be),

The lov - ing Christ (The lov - ing Christ), The Son of God!
That dis - tant day (That dis - tant day), By His own word!
"For - sak - ing all ("For - sak - ing all), O fol - low Me!"

CHORUS

O mem - o - ry, blest mem-o-ry, That takes us back to Gal - i - lee!

Where oft our Lord (Where oft our Lord) at e - ven trod, . . There to com-

mune (There to com - mune) in prayer with God! . .

39 SING AND SMILE AND PRAY

Dedicated to our good friend, Homer A. Rodeheaver

Virgil P. Brock

Blanche Kerr Brock

1. Sing the clouds a - way, night will turn to day; If you sing and
2. Smile the clouds a - way, night will turn to day; If you smile and
4. Sing and smile and pray, that's the on - ly way; If you sing and

sing and sing, You'll sing the clouds a - way.
smile and smile, You'll smile the clouds a - way. 3. Pray the clouds a - way,
smile and pray, You'll drive the clouds a - way.

FINE

D. C. 4th verse

Pray and pray and pray; Night will turn to day, No mat-ter what they say.

40 WHEN I SHALL FALL ASLEEP

Moses Gage Shirley

Chas. H. Gabriel

1. Some day the sun of life will set, and I shall fall a-sleep,
2. Some day the cares of life will cease, and I shall fall a-sleep,
3. Some day my work will all be done, and I shall fall a-sleep,

And, leav-ing all that I hold dear, will find the si-lence deep, —
And, pass-ing from you, I shall see a-far the gold-en street,
But O what joy to know that I shall wake to nev-er weep!

That mys-ter-y which, still un-solved, God and His an-gels know,
And saint-ed forms of those who dwell up-on the oth-er shore,
For where I go we know that God has prom-ised per-fect rest

(And those who walk by crys-tal streams where heav'n-ly breez-es blow,)
Be-hold the loved ones who from us a-while have gone be-fore,
And peace for ev-'ry ach-ing heart, and ev-'ry trou-bled breast;

Where grief nor sor-row ev-er come, nor trou-ble's bil-lows sweep;
Where soft and cool-ing path-ways lie, where none shall ev-er weep;
And love more last-ing than our own He'll give to me to keep,

WHEN I SHALL FALL ASLEEP

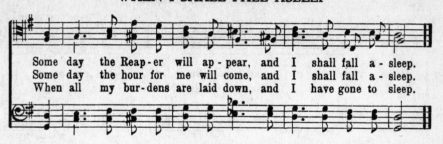

Some day the Reap-er will ap-pear, and I shall fall a-sleep.
Some day the hour for me will come, and I shall fall a-sleep.
When all my bur-dens are laid down, and I have gone to sleep.

41 MOTHER'S PRAYERS HAVE FOLLOWED ME

Lizzie DeArmond

B. D. Ackley

1. I grieved my Lord from day to day, I scorned His love so full and free,
2. O'er des-ert wild, o'er mountain high, A wan-der-er I chose to be,
3. He turned my dark-ness in-to light, This bless-ed Christ of Cal-va-ry;

And tho' I wan-dered far a-way, My moth-er's prayers have followed me.
A wretch-ed soul, con-demned to die, Still moth-er's prayers have followed me.
I'll praise His name both day and night, That mother's prayers have followed me.

REFRAIN

I'm com-ing home, I'm com-ing home, To live my wast-ed life a-new,

For moth-er's prayers have followed me, Have followed me the whole world thru.

WHISPERING HOPE

Alice Hawthorne

1. Soft as the voice of an an - gel Breath-ing a les - son un - heard,
2. If in the dusk of the twi - light Dim be the re - gion a - far,

Hope, with a gen - tle per - sua - sion, Whis-pers her com-fort-ing word.
Will not the deep-en - ing dark - ness Bright-en the glim-mer-ing star?

Wait till the dark-ness is o - ver, Wait till the tem-pest is done, . .
Then when the night is up - on us, Why should the heart sink a - way? . .

rit.

is done,
sink a - way?

Hope for the sun-shine to - mor - row, Aft - er the show-er is gone. . .
When the dark mid-night is o - ver, Watch for the breaking of day. . .

CHORUS

Whis-per - ing hope, whis - per -ing hope, Wel - come thy

Whis - - - - per - ing hope, . . . Oh, how wel - - -

WHISPERING HOPE

Mak - - - ing my voice, wel-come thy voice, Mak - ing my heart,

- - come thy voice, ...

heart ...

mak - ing my heart in its sor - - row re - joice. ...

43 BETHANY BLESSING

Carrie Stewart-Besserer

B. D. Ackley

Ac - cept our grat - i - tude, Lord, For all the bless - ings Thou dost give; Di - rect and guide our dai - ly paths, And teach us how to live, For Je - sus' sake, A - men.

44 HEARTACHES

A. H. A.   Rev. A. H. Ackley

1. When your heart is ach-ing, turn to Je-sus, He's the dear-est
2. There is joy for ev-'ry blight-ing sor-row, Sweet re-lief for
3. Je-sus un-der-stands, what-e'er the trou-ble, And He waits to

friend that you can know; You will find Him stand-ing close be-side you,
ev-'ry bit-ter pain; Je-sus Christ is still the Great Phy-si-cian;
heal your wound-ed soul; Will you trust His love so strong and ten-der?

CHORUS

Wait-ing peace and com-fort to be-stow.
No one ev-er sought His help in vain. Heart-aches, take them all to
He a-lone can make your spir-it whole.

Je-sus, Go to Him to-day, do it now with-out de-lay; Heart-aches,

take them all to Je-sus, He will take your heart-aches all a-way.

45 THE KING OF MY HEART IS JESUS

COPYRIGHT 1908, RENEWAL 1936
THE RODEHEAVER CO., OWNER
INTERNATIONAL COPYRIGHT SECURED

A. H. Ackley

B. D. Ackley

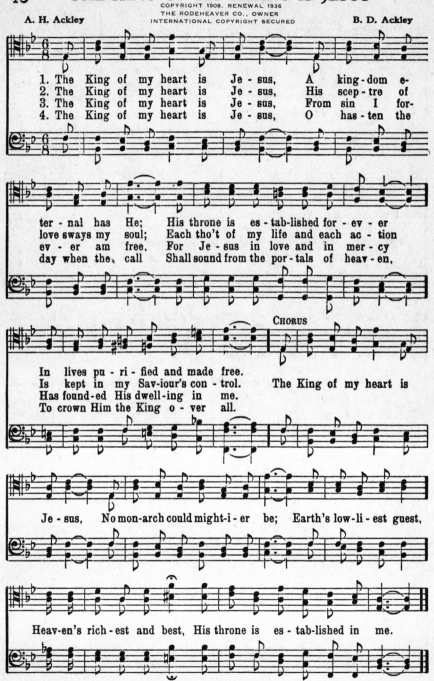

1. The King of my heart is Je - sus, A king-dom e-
2. The King of my heart is Je - sus, His scep-tre of
3. The King of my heart is Je - sus, From sin I for-
4. The King of my heart is Je - sus, O has-ten the

ter - nal has He; His throne is es - tab-lished for - ev - er
love sways my soul; Each tho't of my life and each ac - tion
ev - er am free, For Je - sus in love and in mer - cy
day when the call Shall sound from the por - tals of heav - en,

In lives pu - ri - fied and made free.
Is kept in my Sav-iour's con - trol.
Has found-ed His dwell-ing in me.
To crown Him the King o - ver all.

CHORUS

The King of my heart is Je - sus, No mon-arch could might-i - er be; Earth's low-li - est guest,

Heav-en's rich - est and best, His throne is es - tab-lished in me.

THE CHURCH IN THE WILDWOOD

W. S. P.

Dr. W. S. Pitts

1. There's a church in the val - ley by the wild - wood, No lov - li - er
2. How.... sweet on a clear Sab - bath morn - ing, To list to the
3. There, close by the church in the val - ley, Lies one that I

place in the dale; No spot is so dear to my child-hood As the
clear ring - ing bell; Its tones so.... sweet - ly are call - ing:—"Oh,
loved so.... well; She sleeps, sweet-ly sleeps 'neath the wil - lows: Dis -

CHORUS

lit - tle brown church in the vale.
come to the church in the vale."
turb not her rest in the vale.

Come to the

Oh, come, come, come, come, come, come, come,

come, come,

church in the wild - - wood, Oh, come to the church in the dale;....

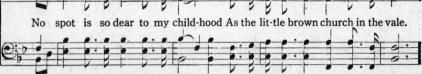

come, come, come, come, come, come, come come, come, come, come, come, come.

D.C.

No spot is so dear to my child-hood As the lit-tle brown church in the vale.

THE CHURCH IN THE WILDWOOD

4. There, close by the side of that loved one 'Neath the tree where the wild flowers bloom,

When the fare-well hymn shall be chant-ed, I shall rest by her side in the tomb.

CHORUS

Oh, come, come, come, come, come, come, come, come, come, come, come, come,

Come to the church in the wild - wood, Oh,

come, come, come, come, No spot is so

come to the church in the vale.................

dear to my child - hood, As the lit - tle brown church in the vale.

47 COULD A LITTLE SUNSHINE

A. H. ACKLEY

B. D. ACKLEY

1. Could a lit-tle bit of sunshine find a place with-in your heart, It would
2. Could a lit-tle bit of sunshine find a place with-in your heart, It would
3. Could a lit-tle bit of sunshine find a place with-in your heart, What a

rift the storm clouds hanging o'er your way; It would soothe the heart of woe, Help an-
light-en care as nothing else can do; It would sweep away a-larm, Keep you
stream of light and glory would be there, It would life and hope re-new, Give you

oth-er joy to know, By the sweetness of its presence day by by.
safe from sin and harm, If the pow-er of its presence dwelt in you.
great-er pow'r to do, For the Mas-ter in His Vineyard ev'ry-where.

CHORUS

'Could a lit-tle bit of sun-shine find a place, to re-flect the

COULD A LITTLE SUNSHINE

wondrous beauties of His grace, It would heal the blight of life, Bring you

peace from sin and strife, Could a lit-tle bit of sunshine find a place.

48 IN REMEMBRANCE

Copyright, 1936, by The Rodeheaver Co.
International Copyright Secured

JULIA BENSON PARKER   B. D. ACKLEY

FINE

1. In   remembrance, Lord, I come, Be - fore Thy ta - ble spread;
2. Bless   the sa - cred bread and cup Of which I now par - take;

D.C.—take a - way the sin that hides From me   Thy glo - rious face.
D.C.—keep me close and true to Thee Till Thou re - turn in - deed.

Of   Thy bo - dy pierced for me, Thy blood so free - ly shed......
Take my heart, 'tis all   I have To give for Thy sweet sake......

Hum   D.C. al Fine

Though un-wor - thy, Lord, am I, Grant me Thy pard-'ning grace, And
Break to me the Bread of Life, My hun - gry soul to feed; And

Hum.

49 I'M GOING ALL THE WAY WITH JESUS

A. H. ACKLEY

B. D. ACKLEY

1. Bow - ing low be-neath the bur - den of the con - flict, Leav - ing
2. When I trav - el thro' the val - ley deep with shad - ows, There will
3. O the tri - umph of that hour when I be - hold Him O - ver

ros - es where the thorns had pierc'd His hand; O the sweetness of His
be a bea - con light as clear as day; It will bright- en up my
yon - der in the glo - ry - land so fair; Thro' the gold - en streets of

touch which heal'd the helpless, As He passed a-long the road to Glo - ry - land.
jour - ney on to glo - ry, All my burdens will in Je- sus roll a - way.
heav - en I will praise Him, And for - ev - er I shall reign with Jesus there.

CHORUS

I'm go-ing all the way with Je - sus, I'm going all the way with Him; Thro' the

heav'nly gates I'll shout in tri- umph, For I've traveled all the way with Him.

THE HARBOR LIGHTS

Words and arrangement
Copyright, 1938, by The Rodeheaver Co.,

Elsie Duncan Yale

Arr. C. Austin Miles

1. O the har-bor lights are shin-ing, Far a-cross our life's wide sea! And the Pi-lot who is guid-ing, Is the Man of Gal-i-lee, Is the Man of Gal-i-lee, And the Pi-lot who is guid-ing, Is the Man of Gal-i-lee.

2. O the har-bor lights are gleam-ing, O'er the roll-ing, rest-less foam, And the helm our Christ is hold-ing, His the hand that guides us home! His the hand that guides us home! And the helm...... our Christ is hold-ing, His the hand that guides us home!

3. O the har-bor lights are shin-ing, O'er the storm-y waves that roll, And our Pi-lot safe is bring-ing, To the home port of the soul! To the home port of the soul! And our Pi-lot safe is bring-ing, To the home port of the soul.

CHRIST BESIDE THE SEA

ELSIE DUNCAN YALE

ADAM GEIBEL

1. Fish - ers, was your toil in vain? Steadfast let your faith re - main,
2. Hark the voice from dis - tant shore, "Fish - ers cast your net once more!"
3. Wait-ing still be - side life's sea, Wait-ing as by Gal - i - lee,

See on yon-der shore He waits you, Je - sus will your heart sus - tain!
Heed Him, He has come to help you, Courage, for the night is o'er!
Eyes of faith may still be - hold Him, Still a pres-ent Help - er, He!

CHORUS

The Mas-ter waits up - on the shore,

He waits............ up - on the shore, Our Help-er as in
He waits............ with words of cheer, Our Comrade is so

A - gain He waits be - side the sea,

days of yore, He waits......... be-side the sea,
near, so near; He (Omit.................................)

in days of yore,
so ver - y near;

the Mas - ter

The Mas - ter of Gal - i - lee! of Gal - i - lee!

waits.

CHRIST BESIDE THE SEA

waits up-on the shore,

up-on the shore, Our Help-er as in days of yore.

52   I SHALL BE SATISFIED

Copyright, 1932, The Rodeheaver Co. owner
International Copyright Secured

LULU JOHNSTON   HAROLD AMADEUS MILLER

Melody

1. I do not ask my way to see   Sav - iour mine;
2. So keep me ev - er by Thy side,   Sav - iour mine;

I on-ly wish my hands to be   clasped in Thine.
And let me in Thy love a-bide,   whol-ly Thine.

Let me feel Thy pres-ence near,   When I fal-ter when I
Grant me here Thy sav-ing grace,   And in heav'n to see Thy

fear, And I shall be sat-is-fied, Sav - iour mine.
face, And I shall be sat-is-fied, Sav - iour mine.

53 THINE FOR SERVICE

L. S. L.

LIDA SHIVERS LEECH

Melody. 2d Tenor

1. I have made my choice to fol - low Christ each day, I am Thine for
2. Let me i - dle not the pre-cious hours a - way, I am Thine for
3. I am Thine for serv - ice till the last glad hour Shall have passed on

serv - ice, Lord; Tho' I some-times fal - ter on the thorn - y way,
serv - ice, Lord; As Thy voice shall bid me, I will go or stay,
earth from me, And I wake to serv - ice of a great - er pow'r,

I am Thine for serv - ice, Lord.
I am Thine for serv - ice, Lord,
Thro' a glad e - ter - ni - ty.

REFRAIN

Melody. 1st Tenor

Thine for serv - ice when the days are drear, Thine for serv - ice when the skies are clear; Thine for serv - ice thro' the com - ing years, I am Thine for serv - ice, Lord.

54 WINNING MEN FOR JESUS

Rev. A. H. ACKLEY   B. D. ACKLEY

1. Win - ning men for Je - sus ev 'ry - where we go, will we be
2. Win - ning men for Je - sus, touched by oth - ers care, will we be
3. Win - ning men for Je - sus in His church to serve, we know it

In - tro - duc - ing them to One they ought to know, and keep on.
Shar - ing in the sor - rows oth - ers have to bear; will we be,
'Tis a glo - rious hon - or no man can de - serve; Oh! keep us

Tell - ing of the good - ness of this roy - al Friend, who will be
Stand - ing by with com - fort, help - ing them to feel, a lov - ing
In that ho - ly serv - ice, faith - ful, brave and strong, for we are

CHORUS

Lead-ing them to fol - low Him un - to the end.
Je - sus is their Sav-iour with sal - va-tion real. } Winning men for Je - sus,
Bound in deathless un-ion, to op-pose the wrong.

Mel.

ev - 'ry-where we go, Till the joy of His sal - va-tion ev - 'ry man shall know.

55 GOD IS LOVE

W. C. POOLE

B. D. ACKLEY

1. A - bove the skies............... of blue I know...............
2. A - bove the skies............... of blue I see,...............
3. A - bove the skies............... of blue, God's love...............

1. A - bove the skies of blue I know

My Fa - ther lives............... who made them so;...............
As last - ing as............... e - ter - ni - ty,...............
Reach - es as far............... as space a - bove;...............

My Fa - ther lives

who made them so;

'Twas Christ the Lord,............... who made them blue, who made them blue,
My Fa - ther's love............... that can - not fail, that can - not fail,
But, best of all,............... I know in me, I know in me

'Twas Christ the Lord,

CHORUS

And He is love—............... His love is true.
But o - ver all............... it shall pre - vail.
God's love has won............... the vic - to - ry.

He is love,...............

And He is love—

He is love,

His love is true,............... He writes His love on skies of blue;

His love is true

GOD IS LOVE

In His love.............. He watch-es you—....................

In His love   He watch-es you—

He is love,.............. His love is true....................

He is love,   His love is true.

56   GOD KNOWS

Copyright, 1927, The Rodeheaver Co. owner
International Copyright Secured

KATHLEEN R. WHEELER   C. AUSTIN MILES

1. What would you do, if storms should break With vio-lence o'er your head?
2. What would you do if one you loved Be-yond your sight had gone?
3. What would you do if earth's firm strand Should crumble at your feet,

And if your plate should emp-ty lie, While all the rest were fed,
And left you here, com-pan-ion-less, Un-cared for, and a-lone?
And ev-'ry-thing should fall a-way That you have found so sweet?

I look away from fears and woes, And answer thus: "God knows, God knows."
I whisper, "Some have felt such woes, But all our trials, God knows, God knows."
And I must trust un-til life's close, The af-ter life, God knows, God knows.

THE CALL

Wм. D. Hudnut

Daniel Protheroe

Quit you like men; be strong. There's a bur-den to bear, There's a

grief to share, There's a heart that breaks 'neath a load of care, But fare ye

Solo or unison

forth with a song, Quit you like men; be strong. There's a bat-tle to

fight, There's a wrong to right, There's a God who bless-es the good with

Tutti.

might, So fare ye forth with a song. Quit you like men, be

THE CALL

strong. There's a work to do, There's a world to make new, There's a

call for men who are brave and true, On, on with a song!......

Quit you like men; be strong. There's a year of grace, There's a

God to face. There's an-oth-er heat in the great world race,

Speed! Speed...... with a song...

58 WE SHALL SHINE AS THE STARS

J. W. V.

J. W VAN DEVENTER

1. We may tar-ry a while here as stran-gers, Un-no-ticed by those who pass
2. We may nev-er be rich in earth's treas-ures, Nor rise on the lad-der of
3. We may live in a tent or a cot-tage, And die in se-clu-sion un-

by; But the Sav-iour will crown us in glo-ry, To shine as the
fame; But the saints will at last be re-ward-ed, Made rich in Im-
known; But the Fa-ther who see-eth in se-cret, Re-mem-bers each

stars of the sky.
man-u-el's name.
one of His own.

CHORUS f

We shall shine as the stars of the morn-ing,
With Je-sus the cru-ci-fied one; We shall rise to be
like Him for-ev-er, E-ter-nal-ly shine as the sun.

* Arranged as duet for 1st Bass and 1st or 2d Tenor, the other parts humming. This arrangement
may be varied at the discretion of the singers

59 MY MOTHER'S OLD BIBLE IS TRUE

E. E. HEWITT

ADAM GEIBEL

Tenors or Basses, or All in Unison

1. I've found that earth's wa-ters will ne'er sat-is-fy, I sought for re-
2. I turned to the Bi-ble, glad ti-dings I read, Of riv-ers un-
3. I read of the mer-cy that brought Him to die, To save guilt-y
4. A-way with the fountains that shine but to mock, A-way with earth's

fresh-ing and cheer; Its cis-terns were bro-ken, its fountains were dry,
fail-ing and bright; Of Christ the Good Shepherd, who safely hath led
sin-ners like me; That now He is liv-ing in glo-ry on high,
per-ish-ing toys; I drink of the wa-ter that flows from the Rock,

CHORUS *p*

Its joys like the dews dis-ap-pear......... My moth--er's old
His flock by the streams of de-light......... My mother's old Bi-ble is
My more than a broth-er to be............ Melody in 1st Bass
I feast up-on in-fi-nite joys.........

f *p* My moth--er's old

Melody in 1st Tenor

Bi-ble is true; From cov--er to cov-er, all true!
true,........... From cov-er to cover, all true, all true! A mes-sage of love,

Bi-ble is true; From cov--er to cov-er, all true!

'Twas sent from a-bove; My moth-er's old Bi-ble is true, it is true.

WHEN I GET HOME

C. A. M.   C. AUSTIN MILES

1. I shall wear a gold-en crown, When I get home; I shall lay my burdens down,
2. All the darkness will be past, When I get home; I shall see the light at last,
3. I shall see my Saviour's face, When I get home; Sing a-gain of saving grace,

pp Home, home, home, home,

When I get home; Clad in robes of glo-ry, I shall sing the sto-ry
When I get home; Light from heaven streaming, O'er my pathway beaming,
When I get home; I shall stand be-fore Him, Glad-ly I'll a-dore Him,

Home, home, home, home,

CHORUS

Of the Lord who bought me, When I get home.
Ev-er guides me on-ward Till I get home.
Ev-er to be with Him, When I get home.

When I get home,
When I get home,

When I get home, All sor-row will be o-ver, When I get home; When
When I get home,

I get home, When I get home, All sor-row will be o-ver, When I get home.
When I get home, When I get home,

61 ROCK OF AGES, CLEFT FOR ME

AUGUSTUS TOPLADY   J. LINCOLN HALL

1. Rock of Ages   cleft for me,   Let me hide   myself in thee;

1. Rock of A - - ges, cleft for me   Let me hide   myself in thee;
2. Could my tears for - ev- er flow,   Could my zeal   no langour know,
3. While I draw this fleeting breath   When my eyes   shall close in death,

1. Let the water   and the blood   From thy wounded side which flowed,

Let the wa - - ter and the blood   From the wound-ed side which flowed,
These for sin   could not a - tone;   Thou must save, and thou a - lone:
When I rise   to worlds unknown,   And be- hold   thee on thy throne,

Be of sin   the double cure,   Save from wrath and make me pure.

Be of sin   the double cure,   Save from wrath and make me pure.
In my hand   no price I bring;   Sim - ply to   thy cross I cling.
Rock of A - - ges, cleft for me,   Let me hide   my-self in thee.

rit. e dim.

Be of sin   the dou - ble cure, Save from wrath and make me pure.
In my hand   no price I bring; Sim - ply to   thy cross I cling.
Rock of A - - ges, cleft for me, Let me hide my-self in thee.

Be of sin, of sin the dou-ble, dou-ble cure,

WHERE MY SAVIOUR LEADS

EDWARD Y. MASON

J. LINCOLN HALL

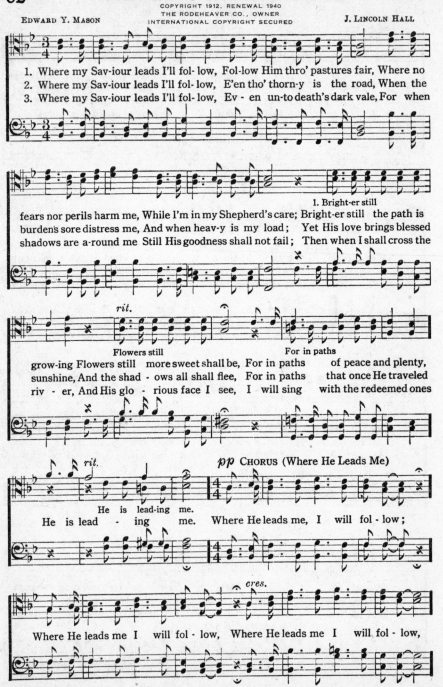

1. Where my Sav-iour leads I'll fol-low, Fol-low Him thro' pastures fair, Where no
2. Where my Sav-iour leads I'll fol-low, E'en tho' thorn-y is the road, When the
3. Where my Sav-iour leads I'll fol-low, Ev - en un-to death's dark vale, For when

fears nor perils harm me, While I'm in my Shepherd's care; Bright-er still the path is
burdens sore distress me, And when heav-y is my load; Yet His love brings blessed
shadows are a-round me Still His goodness shall not fail; Then when I shall cross the

1. Bright-er still

Flowers still   *For in paths*

grow-ing Flowers still more sweet shall be, For in paths of peace and plenty,
sunshine, And the shad - ows all shall flee, For in paths that once He traveled
riv - er, And His glo - rious face I see, I will sing with the redeemed ones

rit.

He is lead-ing me.

He is lead - ing me. Where He leads me, I will fol - low;

pp CHORUS (Where He Leads Me)

cres.

Where He leads me I will fol - low, Where He leads me I will fol - low,

WHERE MY SAVIOUR LEADS

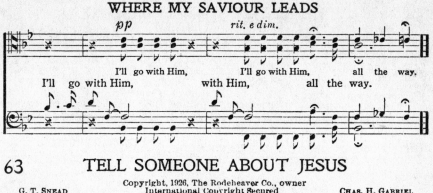

I'll go with Him, with Him, all the way.

I'll go with Him, I'll go with Him, all the way.

63 TELL SOMEONE ABOUT JESUS

G. T. SNEAD   CHAS. H. GABRIEL

1. Go tell someone a-bout Je - sus! Be swift His command to o - bey;
2. Go tell someone a-bout Je - sus! Go tell of His won-der - ful love;
3. Go tell someone a-bout Je - sus! Bring souls out of darkness to light;

Pro-claim un - to all His sal - va - tion, Go now, and no long-er de - lay.
Go tell how He came from His glo - ry— The home of the Father a - bove.
From byways and highways go lead them To paths that are sunny and bright.

CHORUS

Tell someone a-bout Je - sus, Ma - - ny are wait-ing to hear;
Ma - ny are wait-ing to hear;..................

rit. e dim.

Ma - ny are sad and dis-cour-aged, Tell them the sto - ry so dear...........
Tell them the sto - ry so dear.

64 THE SINNER AND THE SONG

W. L. T.

WILL L. THOMPSON
Arr. by PAUL BECKWITH

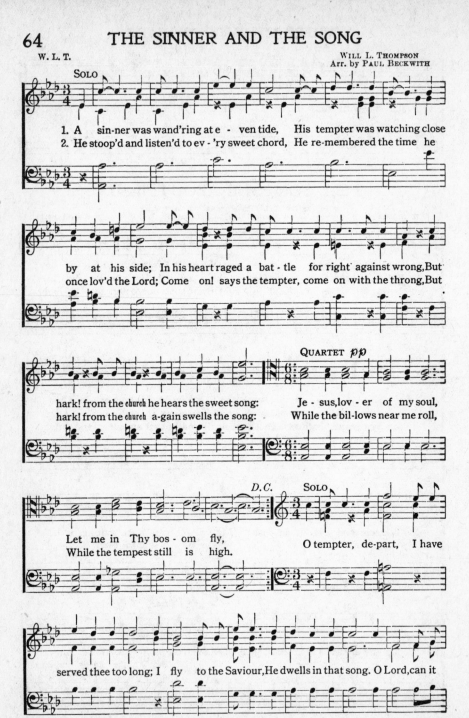

1. A sin-ner was wand'ring at e - ven tide, His tempter was watching close by at his side; In his heart raged a bat - tle for right against wrong, But hark! from the church he hears the sweet song:

2. He stoop'd and listen'd to ev - 'ry sweet chord, He re-membered the time he once lov'd the Lord; Come on! says the tempter, come on with the throng, But hark! from the church a-gain swells the song:

QUARTET *pp*

Je - sus, lov - er of my soul, While the bil-lows near me roll, Let me in Thy bos - om fly, While the tempest still is high.

D.C.

SOLO

O tempter, de-part, I have served thee too long; I fly to the Saviour, He dwells in that song. O Lord, can it

THE SINNER AND THE SONG

be that a sin-ner like me, May find a sweet refuge by com-ing to Thee?

QUARTET   SOLO

Oth - er ref-uge have I none, Hangs my helpless soul on Thee. I

QUARTET *pp*

come, Lord, I come, Thou'lt forgive the dark past, And   Oh, receive my soul at last.

65   SOFTLY NOW THE LIGHT OF DAY

G. W. DOANE   L. M. GOTTSCHALK

1. Soft - ly now the light of day   Fades up - on my sight a - way;
2. Soon, for me the light of day,   Shall for - ev - er pass a - way;
3. Thou, who, sin - less, yet hast known   All of man's in - firm - i - ty;

Free from care, from la - bor free,   Lord I would commune with Thee.
Then, from sin and sor - row free,   Take me, Lord, to dwell with Thee.
Then, from Thine e - ter - nal throne,   Je - sus, look with pity - ing eye.

THE OLD RUGGED CROSS

G. B.

Rev. Geo. Bennard
Arr. D. P.

1. On a hill far a-way stood an old rug-ged cross, The em-blem of
2. Oh, that old rug-ged cross, so de-spised by the world, Has a won-drous at -
3. In the old rug-ged cross, stained with blood so divine, A won - drous
4. To the old rug-ged cross I will ev - er be true, Its shame and re -

suf-f'ring and shame, And I love that old cross where the Dear - est and Best
trac-tion for me; For the dear Lamb of God left His glo - ry a - bove,
beau-ty I see; For 'twas on that old cross Je - sus suf - fered and died,
proach gladly bear; Then He'll call me some day to my home far a - way,

CHORUS

For a world of lost sin-ners was slain. So I'll cher - ish the cross, the
To bear it to dark Cal - va - ry.
To par - don and sanc - ti - fy me.
Where His glo-ry for - ev - er I'll share. 'So I'll cher - ish the old rug - ged

old rug-ged cross, Till my tro-phies at last I lay down; I will cling to the
cross,

old rug - ged cross,............ And exchange it some day for a crown.
cross, the old rug - ged cross,

COME IN

MARGARET ADAMS

ETHEL WAKEFIELD
Arr. D. P.

1. O Sav-iour, Thou art pa-tient still, Tho' I have grieved Thee sore,
2. I see Thee yon-der on the cross, And hear Thy pray'r for me—
3. I yield at last, O bless-ed One, The door stands o-pen wide!

Have slight-ed Thee, be-trayed and De-nied Thee o'er and o'er;
O love, O grace a-maz-ing! Dear Lord, how can it be?
Be-hold, and hear me plead-ing With Thee, to come in-side.

Yet in Thy mer-cy wide and deep Thou hast not turned a-way,
It was my sins that nailed Thee there, And Thou didst take my place
Thy name shall be my sweet-est song, My joy, my pride, my boast;

FINE

For, lo! I find Thee wait-ing Out-side my door to-day.
To die for my trans-gres-sions, And for the hu-man race.
Came in, come, Ab-ba Fa-ther, Come, Son and Ho-ly Ghost.

D.S.—For O I need, I need Thee, Whom once I cru-ci-fied.

CHORUS

D.S.

Come in, Come in, Too long have I de-nied,
O, Lord come in, To cleanse my sin,

68   HE LED ARIGHT

HERMAN VON BERGE   DANIEL PROTHEROE

1. I trust-ed in Him for guid-ance And help up-on my
2. Be-fore His throne I'm bow-ing In grat-i-tude and

way, And He, in His lov-ing kind-ness, Has led me day by
praise To Him who will nev-er fail me Un-to the end of

day. I oft-en would not have cho-sen The paths that He bade me
days. To Him will I leave the guid-ing Thro' what re-mains for

go; But e'en tho' His ways seemed hid-den, He led a-
me; Un-til at the jour-ney's end-ing, with Him at

right, I know, He led a-right, I know.
home I'll be, With Him at home I'll be.

MY GUIDING STAR

Rev. Chas. W. Collinge
2D. Tenor

B. D. Ackley

All Parts

1. My Guid-ing Star shines for me in-to night, And oh, the light!
2. My Guid-ing Star shines for me in-to day, To light the way,
3. And when at last the eve-ning time shall spread A-bout my bed,

2D. Tenor

And oh, the light! Once deep-est dark-ness veiled the way I went,
To light the way, For when the world so fills my wea-ry eyes,
A-bout my bed; When mur-mured low the part-ings and the heart

All Parts   2D. Tenor

My Star was sent, My Star was sent; And now, e'en in the gloaming
And His dear skies, And His dear skies So far a-way, sweet Star, I
For-gets its part, For-gets its part; Then, out the dawn-ing new, be-

All Parts

as I go, I see His glow, I see His glow; And now, e'en in the
need Thy ray To light my day, To light my day; So far a-way, sweet
yond, a-far, Shall shine my Star, Shall shine my Star; Then, out the dawn-ing

gloam-ing as I go, I see His glow, I see His glow.
Star, I need Thy ray To light my day, To light my day.
new, be-yond, a-far, Shall shine my Star, Shall shine my Star.

70 SOMEBODY CARES

FANNIE EDNA STAFFORD

HOMER RODEHEAVER
Arr. D. P.

1. Some-bod-y knows when your heart aches, And ev-'ry-thing seems to go wrong; Some-bod-y knows when the shad-ows Need chas-ing a-way with a song; Some-bod-y knows when you're lone-ly, Tired, dis-cour-aged and blue; Some-bod-y wants you to know Him, And know that He dear-ly loves you.

2. Some-bod-y knows when you're tempt-ed, And your mind grows diz-zy and dim; Some-bod-y cares when you're weak-est, And far-thest a-way from Him; Some-bod-y grieves when you've fall-en, You are not lost from His sight; Some-bod-y waits for your com-ing, And He'll drive the gloom from your night.

3. Some-bod-y loves you when wea-ry; Some-bod-y loves you when strong; Al-ways is wait-ing to help you, He watch-es you—one of the throng Need-ing His friendship so ho-ly Need-ing His watch-care so true; His name? we call His name Je-sus; He loves ev-'ry one, He loves you.

71 THE SHEPHERD TRUE

F. W. FABER

GEO. C. STEBBINS

1. I was wand'ring, sad and wea - ry, When the Sav - iour came un - to me;
2. At first I would not heark - en, But put off till the mor - row,
3. At last I stopped to list - en— His voice could ne'er de-ceive me;—
4. I thought His love would weak - en As more and more He knew me,

For the paths of sin were drear - y, And the world had ceased to woo me;
Till life be - gan to dark - en, And I grew sick with sor - row;
I saw His kind eye glis - ten, So anx - ious to re - lieve me;
But it burn - eth like a bea - con, And its light and heat go thro' me;

And I tho't I heard Him say, As He came a - long His way,—
And I tho't I heard Him say, As He came a - long His way,—
Then I knew I heard Him say, As He came a - long His way,—
And I ev - er hear Him say, As He goes a - long His way,—

REFRAIN *First 2 lines of 2d Tenor prominent*

Wand'ring soul. O do come near Me; My sheep should nev - er

rit.   p   pp

fear Me; I am the Shep-herd true, I am the Shep-herd true.

TILL THE WHOLE WORLD KNOWS

A. H. ACKLEY

B. D. ACKLEY
Arr. D. P.

Melody in 2nd Tenor

1. I'll tell to all that God is love: For the world has nev-er known
2. I'll tell of mer-cy's bound-less tide, Like the wa-ters of the sea,
3. I'll tell of grace that keeps the soul, Of a-bid-ing grace with-in,
4. E-ter-nal glo-ry is the goal That a-waits the sons of light;

The great com-pas-sion of His heart For the way-ward and the lone.
That cov-ers ev-'ry sin of man; 'Tis sal-va-tion full and free.
Of faith that o-ver-comes the world, With its tu-mult and its din.
E-ter-nal dark-ness, black as death, For the chil-dren of the night.

CHORUS

Till the whole world knows, Till the whole world
Till the world, till the whole world knows, Till the world, till the world, the

Till the world, the whole world knows, Till the whole world

knows, I will shout and sing Of Christ my King, Till the whole world knows.
whole world knows,

knows,

73 HIDE ME, LORD, IN THY PAVILION!

Rev. Frank W. Gunsaulus, D.D.

R. H. Pritchard
Arr. D. P.

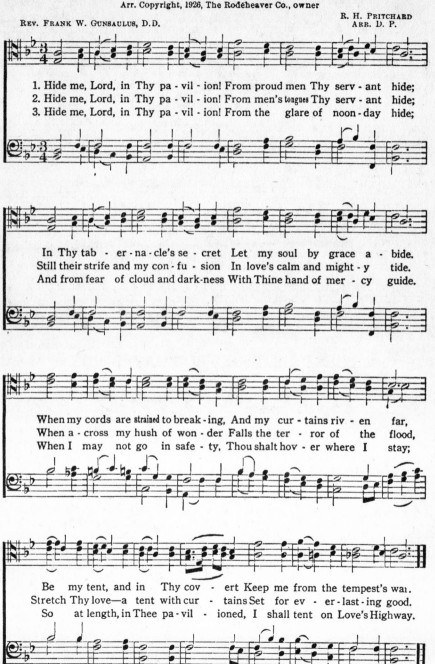

1. Hide me, Lord, in Thy pa - vil - ion! From proud men Thy serv - ant hide;
2. Hide me, Lord, in Thy pa - vil - ion! From men's tongues Thy serv - ant hide;
3. Hide me, Lord, in Thy pa - vil - ion! From the glare of noon - day hide;

In Thy tab - er - na - cle's se - cret Let my soul by grace a - bide.
Still their strife and my con - fu - sion In love's calm and might - y tide.
And from fear of cloud and dark-ness With Thine hand of mer - cy guide.

When my cords are strained to break - ing, And my cur - tains riv - en far,
When a - cross my hush of won - der Falls the ter - ror of the flood,
When I may not go in safe - ty, Thou shalt hov - er where I stay;

Be my tent, and in Thy cov - ert Keep me from the tempest's war.
Stretch Thy love—a tent with cur - tains Set for ev - er - last - ing good.
So at length, in Thee pa - vil - ioned, I shall tent on Love's Highway.

NOW THE DAY IS OVER

SABINE BARING GOULD

J. BARNBY

1. Now the day is o - ver, Night is draw - ing nigh.........
2. Je - sus, give the wea - ry Calm and sweet re - pose;.......
3. Grant to lit - tle chil - dren Vis - ions bright of Thee;......
4. Thro' the long night watch - es May Thine an - gels spread .....
5. When the morn-ing wak - ens, Then may I a - rise.........

Shad - ows of the eve - ning Steal a - cross the sky.
With Thy ten- d'rest bless - ing May mine eye - lids close.
Guard the sail - ors toss - ing On the deep, blue sea.
Their white wings a - bove me, Watch - ing round my bed.
Pure, and fresh, and sin - less In Thy ho - ly eyes.

eve - ning steal a - cross the sky.
bless - ing may our eye - lids close.

75 BLEST BE THE TIE THAT BINDS

REV. JOAN FAWCETT

LOWELL MASON

1. Blest be the tie that binds Our hearts in Chris-tian love: The
2. Be - fore our Fa-ther's throne We pour our ar - dent pray'rs; Our
3. We share our mu - tual woes, Our mu - tual bur - dens bear; And
4. When we a - sun - der part, It gives us in - ward pain; But

fel - low - ship of kin - dred minds Is like to that a - bove.
fears, our hopes, our aims are one, Our com - forts and our cares.
oft - en for each oth - er flows The sym - pa - thiz - ing tear.
we shall still be joined in heart, And hope to meet a - gain.

LEAD, KINDLY LIGHT

John H. Newman

John B. Dykes

1. Lead kind-ly Light, a-mid th'en-cir-cling gloom, Lead Thou me on! The night is dark, and I am far from home; Lead Thou me on! Keep Thou my feet; I do not ask to see. The dis-tant scene; one step e-nough for me.

2. I was not ev-er thus, nor prayed that Thou Should'st lead me on; I loved to choose and see my path; but now Lead Thou me on! I loved the gar-ish day; and, spite of fears, Pride ruled my will. Re-mem-ber not past years!

3. So long Thy pow'r hath blest me sure it still Will lead me on O'er moor and fen, o'er crag and tor-rent, till The night is gone; And with the morn those an-gel fa-ces smile, Which I have loved long since and lost a-while.

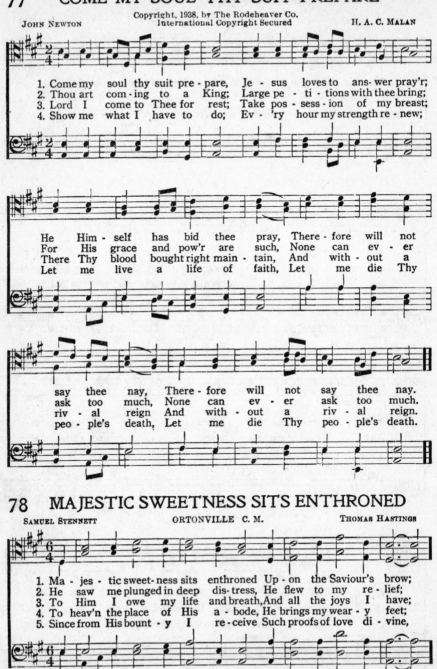

77 COME MY SOUL THY SUIT PREPARE

JOHN NEWTON

H. A. C. MALAN

1. Come my soul thy suit pre - pare, Je - sus loves to ans- wer pray'r;
2. Thou art com - ing to a King; Large pe - ti - tions with thee bring;
3. Lord I come to Thee for rest; Take pos - sess - ion of my breast;
4. Show me what I have to do; Ev - 'ry hour my strength re - new;

He Him - self has bid thee pray, There - fore will not
For His grace and pow'r are such, None can ev - er
There Thy blood bought right main - tain, And with - out a
Let me live a life of faith, Let me die Thy

say thee nay, There - fore will not say thee nay.
ask too much, None can ev - er ask too much.
riv - al reign And with - out a riv - al reign.
peo - ple's death, Let me die Thy peo - ple's death.

78 MAJESTIC SWEETNESS SITS ENTHRONED

SAMUEL STENNETT

ORTONVILLE C. M.

THOMAS HASTINGS

1. Ma - jes - tic sweet- ness sits enthroned Up - on the Saviour's brow;
2. He saw me plunged in deep dis- tress, He flew to my re - lief;
3. To Him I owe my life and breath, And all the joys I have;
4. To heav'n the place of His a - bode, He brings my wear - y feet;
5. Since from His bount - y I re - ceive Such proofs of love di - vine,

MAJESTIC SWEETNESS SITS ENTHRONED

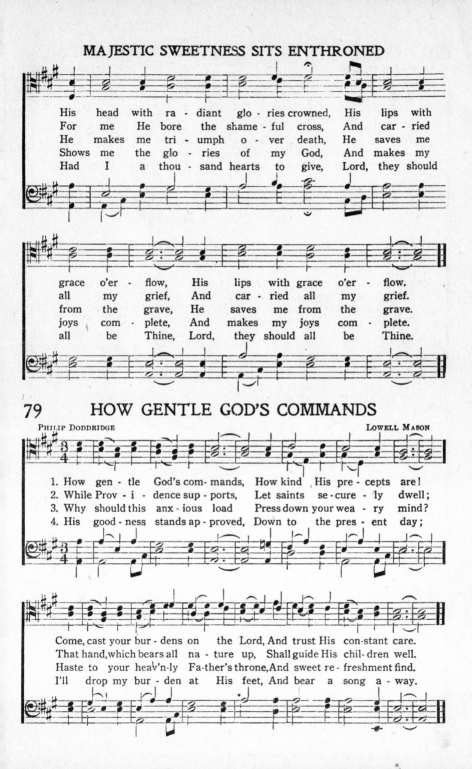

His head with ra - diant glo - ries crowned, His lips with
For me He bore the shame - ful cross, And car - ried
He makes me tri - umph o - ver death, He saves me
Shows me the glo - ries of my God, And makes my
Had I a thou - sand hearts to give, Lord, they should

grace o'er - flow, His lips with grace o'er - flow.
all my grief, And car - ried all my grief.
from the grave, He saves me from the grave.
joys com - plete, And makes my joys com - plete.
all be Thine, Lord, they should all be Thine.

79 HOW GENTLE GOD'S COMMANDS

PHILIP DODDRIDGE   LOWELL MASON

1. How gen - tle God's com - mands, How kind His pre - cepts are!
2. While Prov - i - dence sup - ports, Let saints se - cure - ly dwell;
3. Why should this anx - ious load Press down your wea - ry mind?
4. His good - ness stands ap - proved, Down to the pres - ent day;

Come, cast your bur - dens on the Lord, And trust His con - stant care.
That hand, which bears all na - ture up, Shall guide His chil - dren well.
Haste to your heav'n - ly Fa - ther's throne, And sweet re - freshment find.
I'll drop my bur - den at His feet, And bear a song a - way.

80 O MASTER, LET ME WALK WITH THEE

Washington Gladden

H. Percy Smith

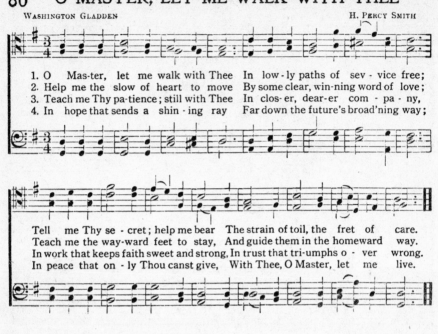

1. O Mas-ter, let me walk with Thee In low-ly paths of sev-vice free;
2. Help me the slow of heart to move By some clear, win-ning word of love;
3. Teach me Thy pa-tience; still with Thee In clos-er, dear-er com-pa-ny,
4. In hope that sends a shin-ing ray Far down the future's broad'ning way;

Tell me Thy se-cret; help me bear The strain of toil, the fret of care.
Teach me the way-ward feet to stay, And guide them in the homeward way.
In work that keeps faith sweet and strong, In trust that tri-umphs o-ver wrong.
In peace that on-ly Thou canst give, With Thee, O Master, let me live.

81 THERE'S A WIDENESS IN GOD'S MERCY

Rev. F. W. Faber

Lizzie S. Tourjee

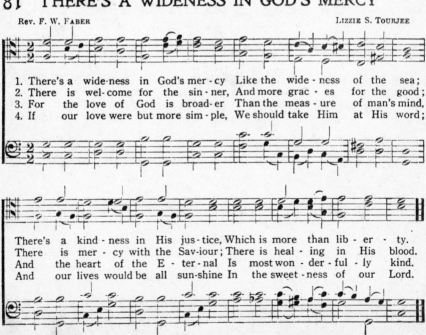

1. There's a wide-ness in God's mer-cy Like the wide-ness of the sea;
2. There is wel-come for the sin-ner, And more grac-es for the good;
3. For the love of God is broad-er Than the meas-ure of man's mind,
4. If our love were but more sim-ple, We should take Him at His word;

There's a kind-ness in His jus-tice, Which is more than lib-er-ty.
There is mer-cy with the Sav-iour; There is heal-ing in His blood.
And the heart of the E-ter-nal Is most won-der-ful-ly kind.
And our lives would be all sun-shine In the sweet-ness of our Lord.

82   NONE OF SELF AND ALL OF THEE

THEODORE MONROE   Copyright, 1912, by L. S. Chafer   Mrs. LEWIS SPERRY CHAFER

1. O the bit - ter pain and sor - row, That a time could ev - er be,
2. Yet He found me I be - held Him Bleed-ing on th'ac-curs-ed tree,
3. Day by day His ten - der mer - cies, Help- ing heal - ing full and free
4. High- er than the high-est heav - en, Deep- er than the deep-est sea,

When I proud - ly said to Je - sus, All of self and none of Thee.
And my wist - ful heart said faint - ly, Some of self and some of Thee.
Brought me low - er while I whis-pered, Less of self and more of Thee.
Lord Thy love at last has conquered, None of self and all of Thee,

All of self and none of Thee, All of self and none of Thee.
Some of self and some of Thee, Some of self and some of Thee.
Less of self and more of Thee, Less of self and more of Thee.
None of self and all of Thee, None of self and all of Thee.

When I proud - ly said to Je - sus, All of self and none of Thee.
And my wist - ful heart said faint - ly, Some of self and some of Thee.
Brought me low - er while I whis-pered, Less of self and more of Thee.
Lord, Thy love at last has con-quered, None of self and all of Thee.

83 JESUS, LOVER OF MY SOUL

CHAS. WESLEY

S. B. MARSH

1. Je - sus, lov - er of my soul, Let me to Thy bos - om fly,
2. Oth - er ref - uge have I none; Hangs my helpless soul on Thee:
3. Thou, O Christ, art all I want; More than all in Thee I find;
4. Plen-teous grace in Thee is found, Grace to cov - er all my sin:

FINE

While the near-er wa - ters roll While the tem-pest still is high!
Leave, ah leave me not a - lone, Still sup-port and com - fort me:
Raise the fall -en, cheer the faint, Heal the sick, and lead the blind.
Let the healing streams abound; Make and keep me pure with - in.

D.S.—*Safe in - to the ha - ven guide, O re-ceive my soul at last!*
D.S.—*Cov - er my de-fense-less head With the shad-ow of Thy wing.*
D.S.—*False and full of sin I am, Thy art full of truth and grace.*
D.S.—*Spring Thou up within my heart, Rise to all e - ter - ni - ty.*

D.S. al Fine

Hide me, O my Sav - iour hide, Till the storm of life is past;
All my trust on Thee is stayed, All my help from Thee I bring;
Just and ho - ly is Thy name, I am all un-right-eous - ness;
Thou of life the fount-ain art, Free-ly let me take of Thee:

84 NEARER MY GOD TO THEE

SARAH F. ADAMS

LOWELL MASON

1. Near - er, my God, to Thee, Near - er to Thee; E'en tho' it
2. Tho' like a wan - der - er, The sun gone down, Dark - ness be
3. There let the way ap - pear Steps un - to heav'n; All that Thou
4. Or if, on joy - ful wing, Cleav-ing the sky, Sun, moon and

NEARER, MY GOD TO THEE

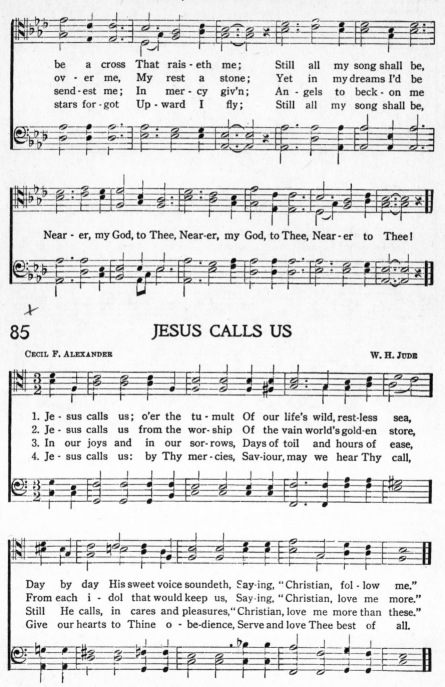

be a cross That rais-eth me; Still all my song shall be,
ov-er me, My rest a stone; Yet in my dreams I'd be
send-est me; In mer-cy giv'n; An-gels to beck-on me
stars for-got Up-ward I fly; Still all my song shall be,

Near-er, my God, to Thee, Near-er, my God, to Thee, Near-er to Thee!

85 JESUS CALLS US

Cecil F. Alexander

W. H. Jude

1. Je-sus calls us; o'er the tu-mult Of our life's wild, rest-less sea,
2. Je-sus calls us from the wor-ship Of the vain world's gold-en store,
3. In our joys and in our sor-rows, Days of toil and hours of ease,
4. Je-sus calls us: by Thy mer-cies, Sav-iour, may we hear Thy call,

Day by day His sweet voice soundeth, Say-ing, "Christian, fol-low me."
From each i-dol that would keep us, Say-ing, "Christian, love me more."
Still He calls, in cares and pleasures, "Christian, love me more than these."
Give our hearts to Thine o-be-dience, Serve and love Thee best of all.

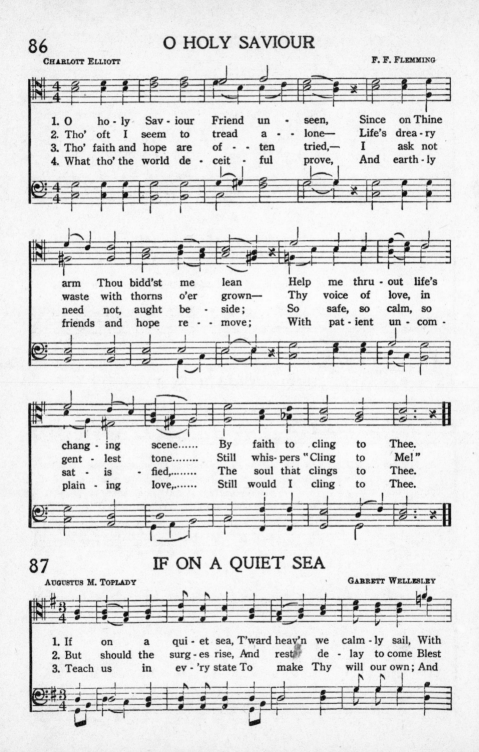

O HOLY SAVIOUR

CHARLOTT ELLIOTT

F. F. FLEMMING

1. O ho-ly Sav-iour Friend un-seen, Since on Thine
2. Tho' oft I seem to tread a--lone— Life's drea-ry
3. Tho' faith and hope are of--ten tried,— I ask not
4. What tho' the world de-ceit-ful prove, And earth-ly

arm Thou bidd'st me lean Help me thru-out life's
waste with thorns o'er grown— Thy voice of love, in
need not, aught be-side; So safe, so calm, so
friends and hope re--move; With pat-ient un-com-

chang-ing scene...... By faith to cling to Thee.
gent-lest tone........ Still whis-pers "Cling to Me!"
sat-is-fied,........ The soul that clings to Thee.
plain-ing love,....... Still would I cling to Thee.

87

IF ON A QUIET SEA

AUGUSTUS M. TOPLADY

GABRETT WELLESLEY

1. If on a qui-et sea, T'ward heav'n we calm-ly sail, With
2. But should the surg-es rise, And rest de-lay to come Blest
3. Teach us in ev-'ry state To make Thy will our own; And

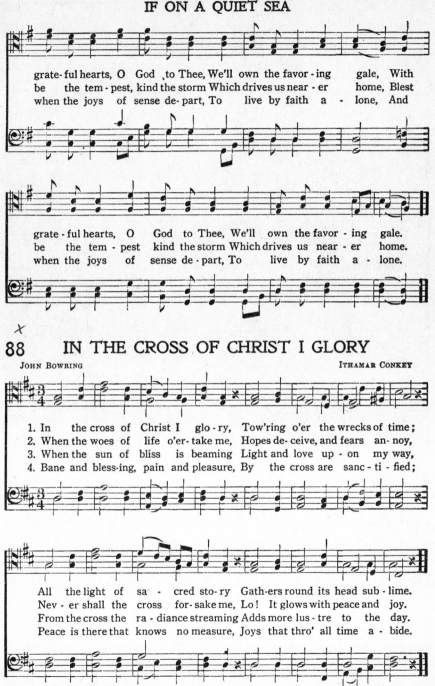

IF ON A QUIET SEA

grate-ful hearts, O God to Thee, We'll own the favor-ing gale, With
be the tem-pest, kind the storm Which drives us near-er home, Blest
when the joys of sense de-part, To live by faith a - lone, And

grate-ful hearts, O God to Thee, We'll own the favor-ing gale.
be the tem-pest kind the storm Which drives us near-er home.
when the joys of sense de-part, To live by faith a - lone.

88 IN THE CROSS OF CHRIST I GLORY

JOHN BOWRING

ITHAMAR CONKEY

1. In the cross of Christ I glo-ry, Tow'ring o'er the wrecks of time;
2. When the woes of life o'er-take me, Hopes de-ceive, and fears an-noy,
3. When the sun of bliss is beaming Light and love up-on my way,
4. Bane and bless-ing, pain and pleasure, By the cross are sanc-ti-fied;

All the light of sa - cred sto-ry Gath-ers round its head sub-lime.
Nev-er shall the cross for-sake me, Lo! It glows with peace and joy.
From the cross the ra-diance streaming Adds more lus-tre to the day.
Peace is there that knows no measure, Joys that thro' all time a - bide.

ALL HAIL THE POWER OF JESUS' NAME

E. PERRONET JAMES ELLOR

1. All hail the pow'r of Je - sus' name! Let an - gels pros-trate
2. Ye cho - sen seed of Is - rael's race, Ye ran-somed from the
3. Let ev - 'ry kin - dred, ev - 'ry tribe, Oh this ter - res - trial
4. O that with yon - der sa - cred throng We at His feet may

fall, Let an - gels pros - trate fall; Bring forth the roy - al
fall, Ye ran-somed from the fall; Hail Him who saves you
ball, On this ter - res - trial ball, To Him all maj - es -
fall, We at His feet may fall! We'll join the ev - er -

di - a - dem, and crown.............................. Him
by His grace and crown.............................. Him
ty as - cribe and crown.............................. Him
last - ing song and crown.............................. Him

crown Him, crown Him, crown Him, crown.................

crown Him, crown Him, crown Him; And crown Him Lord of all!

And crown Him Lord of all!

90 A PLACE AT THE CROSS

H. L.

HALDOR LILLENAS

1. Sin - ner, poor sin - ner, why wan - der a - way, There's a place at the
2. Je - sus has suf - fered and died for us all, There's a place at the
3. Bring all your bur - dens to lay at His feet, There's a place at the
4. Tho' you have wandered a - way from His fold, There's a place at the

Melody in 1st Bass

cross for thee; O heed now the Spir - it, seek par-don to - day, There's a
cross for thee; O hast- en my bro-ther and come at His call, There's a
cross for thee; There's pardon for you and redemption complete, There's a
cross for thee; Come back from the mountains so bar- ren and cold, There's a

CHORUS

Melody in 2d Tenor

place at the cross for thee. There's a place at the cross for
for thee.

thee,...... There's a place at the cross for thee;...... O do not de -
for thee, for thee;

Melody in 1st Bass

lay, but come while you may, There's a place at the cross for thee........
for thee.

Melody in 2d Tenor

* Small notes may be hummed

91 MEET ME IN THE HOMELAND

T. D. A.

T. D. Abels

1. There's a bless-ed Home-land waiting o-ver there. Where the Saviour said a
2. Wea-ry soul, and burdened, sink not in de-spair; Rest and peace and joy are
3. Heav-en, aft-er all, is not so far a-way: Just a mo-ment takes us
4. Sin-ner, come to Je-sus, trust His pow'r to save; Let the eye of faith look

man-sion He'd pre-pare For the ones who seek His sav-ing grace to know,
wait-ing o-ver there; Morn-ing fol-lows all the dark-ness of the night,
out of yes-ter-day; In a mo-ment more to-mor-row's light we'll see;
far be-yond the grave: Loved ones gone be-fore us beck-on us to come

CHORUS

Trust-ing in His keep-ing here be-low.
He will sure-ly keep you by His might. Meet me in the Home-land
In a mo-ment heav'n will dawn on me.
To the place that's wait-ing in that Home.

where the flow-ers bloom; Where there nev-er en-ters sor-row, death nor gloom:

All is fair and bright in that blest home on high: Meet me in the Homeland by and by.

92 LAUNCH OUT INTO THE DEEP

T. D. A.

T. D. Abels

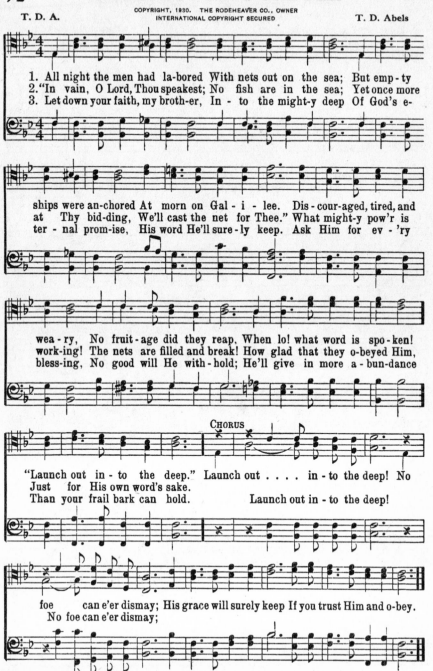

1. All night the men had la-bored With nets out on the sea; But emp-ty
2. "In vain, O Lord, Thou speakest; No fish are in the sea; Yet once more
3. Let down your faith, my broth-er, In - to the might-y deep Of God's e-

ships were an-chored At morn on Gal - i - lee. Dis - cour-aged, tired, and
at Thy bid-ding, We'll cast the net for Thee." What might-y pow'r is
ter - nal prom-ise, His word He'll sure-ly keep. Ask Him for ev - 'ry

wea - ry, No fruit-age did they reap, When lo! what word is spo - ken!
work-ing! The nets are filled and break! How glad that they o-beyed Him,
bless-ing, No good will He with - hold; He'll give in more a - bun-dance

CHORUS

"Launch out in - to the deep." Launch out . . . . in - to the deep! No
Just for His own word's sake.
Than your frail bark can hold. Launch out in - to the deep!

foe can e'er dismay; His grace will surely keep If you trust Him and o-bey.
No foe can e'er dismay;

THE CITY UNSEEN

Emma Tuttle

From James G. Clark
Arr. by Norman Price

DUET FOR BARITONE AND TENOR

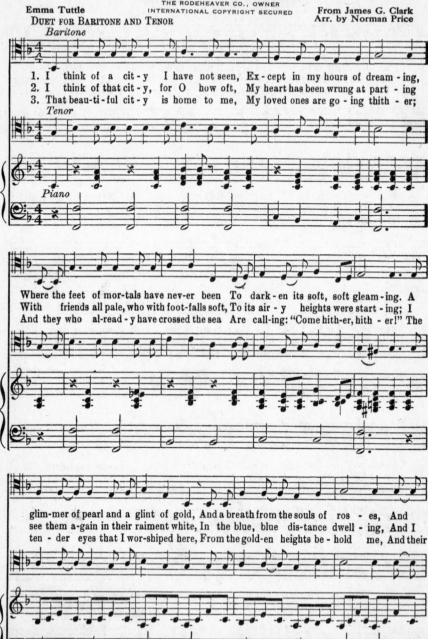

1. I think of a cit-y I have not seen, Ex-cept in my hours of dream-ing,
2. I think of that cit-y, for O how oft, My heart has been wrung at part-ing
3. That beau-ti-ful cit-y is home to me, My loved ones are go-ing thith-er;

Where the feet of mor-tals have nev-er been To dark-en its soft, soft gleam-ing. A
With friends all pale, who with foot-falls soft, To its air-y heights were start-ing; I
And they who al-read-y have crossed the sea Are call-ing: "Come hith-er, hith-er!" The

glim-mer of pearl and a glint of gold, And a breath from the souls of ros-es, And
see them a-gain in their raiment white, In the blue, blue dis-tance dwell-ing, And I
ten-der eyes that I wor-shiped here, From the gold-en heights be-hold me, And their

THE CITY UNSEEN

glo - ry and beau - ty   all   un-told Steals o - ver my calm re - pos - es.
hear their prais - es in calm de-light Come down on the breez - es   swell - ing.
songs en - trance my   rap - tured ear When the wings of   slum - ber   fold   me.

CHORUS

As I dream.................................... Of a   cit - y   I
As I dream of a cit - y   I have not seen,

have not   seen, As I dream.. Of a
As I dream of a cit - y   I have not seen, As I

cit - y   I have not   seen,   Of a   cit - y   I have   not seen.
dream.....................

94 THE GATE AJAR

S. J. Vail

Hum

1. There is a gate that stands a - jar, And thru its por-tals gleam-ing,
2. That gate a-jar stands free for all Who seek thru it sal - va - tion;
3. Press onward then, tho' foes may frown, While mercy's gate is o - pen;

Hum

Hum

A ra-diance from the cross a - far The Sav-iour's love re - veal - ing.
The rich and poor, the great and small, Of ev - 'ry tribe and na - tion.
Ac - cept the cross, and win the crown, Love's ev - er - last - ing to - ken.

Hum

CHORUS

O depths of mer-cy! can it be That gate was left a - jar for me? For me,
For me, . . for

Mel.

f | 1st and 2d verses | Last time only *pp*

for me, Was left a - jar for me? left a - jar for me?
me, . . .

f | *pp*

*Dim. e rit. ad lib. to pp: pause; then, almost in a whisper, sing "for me."

WE'RE HOMEWARD BOUND

J. B. Herbert

1. Out on an o - cean all bound-less we ride, We're home-ward bound,
2. Wild - ly the storm sweeps us on as it roars, We're home-ward bound,

we're home-ward bound; Tossed on the waves of a rough, rest-less tide;
we're home-ward bound; Look! yon-der lie the bright heav-en - ly shores;

We're home-ward bound, home-ward bound. Far from the safe, qui - et
We're home-ward bound, home-ward bound. Stead-y! O pi - lot, stand

har - bor we rode, Seek-ing our Fa-ther's a - bode; . . . .
firm at the wheel, Soon we'll out-weath-er the gale; . . . .

Promise of which on us each He bestowed; We're homeward bound, homeward bound.
O how we fly 'neath the loud creaking sail; We're homeward bound, homeward bound.

*"Ah" may be used instead of humming.

MEN OF VALOR

C. H. G.

CHAS. H. GABRIEL

PRELUDE

1. Men of val - or, of all a - ges, Join the con - flict as it
2. Men of val - or, sin as - sail - ing With no fear of weak - ly
3. Men of val - or, rise in num - ber! In your tents no lon - ger

ra - ges; Young and old the fight en - gag - es, Lend now your aid!
fail - ing, 'Tis the tho't of right pre - vail - ing Strengthens the arm.
slum - ber,- Nor the val - iant hosts en - cum - ber, Rouse ye, be true!

Sounds of tu - mult now are near - ing; Might - y is the foe ap -
"God and home" the watchword ev - er; Chains of e - vil you must
See! the heart of sin is quak - ing! Her de - fense is sure - ly

pear - ing; On-ward go, in spite of jeer - ing, Be not a - fraid!
sev - er; Du - ty calls! be faith - less nev - er,— God shields from harm!
break - ing! To your du - ty then a - wak - ing, God calls for you.

MEN OF VALOR

CHORUS

Bu-gles call-ing, Foes are fall - ing! Brave-ly now de-fend the
Bu-gles call-ing   Foes are fall - ing!   Brave-ly now de-

right!   Souls are plead-ing,   Cour-age need-ing,   You must
fend the right!   For   souls are plead-ing,   Cour-age need-ing,

help   to   win   the fight!   Christ o - bey - ing,   Nor de-
You must help   to   win   the fight!   Christ o - bey - ing,

lay - ing,   To   the front in haste a - way!   Be a-
Nor de - lay - ing,   To   the   front in haste, a - way!

sol - dier true; There is need of   you   In   the ranks   to - day.

JESUS LOVER OF MY SOUL

Arr. Copyright, 1938, by The Rodeheaver Co.
International Copyright Secured

CHARLES WESLEY

1. Je - sus Lov - er of my soul, Let me to Thy bos - om fly, While the
2. Plenteous grace with Thee is found, Grace to par - don all my sin, Let the

bil - - lows near me roll, While the tem - - pest still is high.
heal - - ing streams a - bound; Make and keep me pure with - in.

Sop. *Obbligato*

Hide me, O my Sav - iour, hide, Till the storm of life is past;
Thou of life the foun - tain art, Free - ly let me take of Thee;

Hide me, O my Sav - iour, hide, Till the storm of life is past;
Thou of life the foun - tain art, Free - ly let me take of Thee;

Safe in - to the ha - ven guide, O re - ceive my soul at last!
Spring Thou up with - in my heart, Rise to all e - ter - ni - ty.

Hum ....

O re - ceive my soul at last!
Rise to all e - ter - ni - ty.

98 FROM EV'RY STORMY WIND THAT BLOWS

HUGH STOWELL · Arr. Copyright, 1938, by The Rodeheaver Co. · THOMAS HASTINGS

1. From ev-'ry storm-y wind that blows, From ev-'ry swell-ing tide of woes, There is a calm, a sure re-treat; 'Tis found beneath the mer-cy seat.

2. There is a place where Je-sus sheds The oil of glad-ness on our heads; A place than all be-sides more sweet: It is the blood-bought mer-cy seat.

Spirituals

99 SOMEBODY'S KNOCKING AT YOUR DOOR

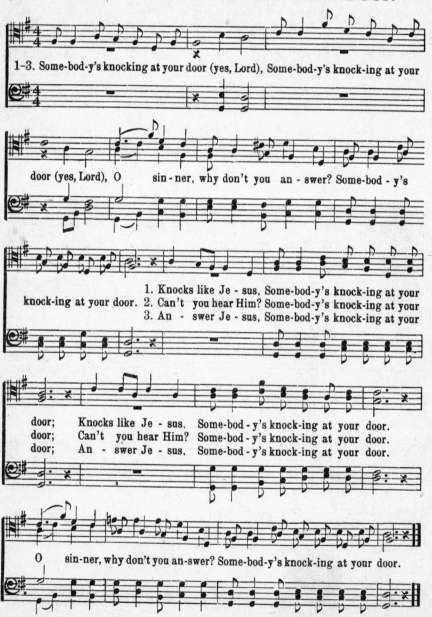

1-3. Some-bod-y's knocking at your door (yes, Lord), Some-bod-y's knock-ing at your door (yes, Lord), O sin-ner, why don't you an-swer? Some-bod-y's knock-ing at your door.

1. Knocks like Je-sus, Some-bod-y's knock-ing at your door; Knocks like Je-sus, Some-bod-y's knock-ing at your door.
2. Can't you hear Him? Some-bod-y's knock-ing at your door; Can't you hear Him? Some-bod-y's knock-ing at your door.
3. An-swer Je-sus, Some-bod-y's knock-ing at your door; An-swer Je-sus, Some-bod-y's knock-ing at your door.

O sin-ner, why don't you an-swer? Some-bod-y's knock-ing at your door.

I'M NEW-BORN AGAIN

Arranged

1. I found free grace and dy-ing love, I'm new-born a-gain;
2. I know my Lord has set me free, I'm new-born a-gain;
3. My Sav-iour died for you and me, I'm new-born a-gain;

Been a long time a-talk-in' 'bout my tri-als here be-low.
Been a long time a-talk-in' 'bout my tri-als here be-low.
Been a long time a-talk-in' 'bout my tri-als here be-low.

Free grace, free grace, free grace, sin-ner, Free grace, free grace, I'm

new-born a-gain. So glad! So glad! I'm new-born a-gain;

Been a long time a-talk-in' 'bout my tri-als here be-low.

101 KING JESUS IS A-LISTENIN'

King Je-sus is a-lis-ten-in', All day long, King Je-sus is a-lis-ten-in', All day long; King Je-sus is a-lis-ten-in', All day long, To hear some sin-ner pray.

Hum

1. Some say that John the Bap-tist Was noth-in' but a Jew, But the
2. That Gos-pel train is com-in', A-rum-blin' thru the land, But I
3. I know I've been con-vert-ed, I ain't goin' to make no a-larm, For my

Ho-ly Bi-ble tells us That John was a preach-er, too.
hear them wheels a-hum-min', Get read-y to board that train!
soul is bound to Je-sus, And the dev-il can't do me no harm.

102 AMEN

Rev. B. H. Hogan.

Rev. B. H. Hogan and Laura B. Davis

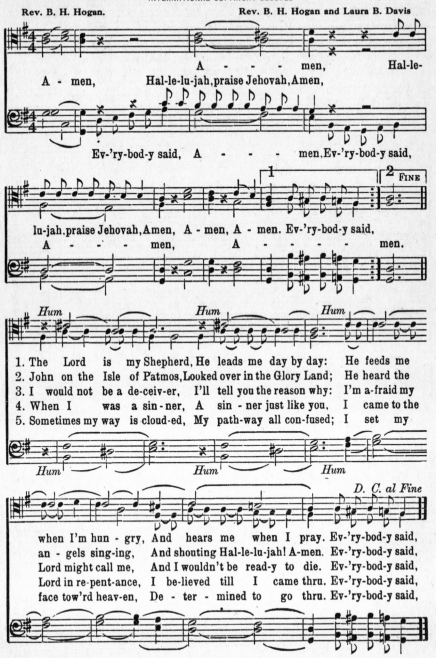

A - - - men, Hal-le-
A - men, Hal-le-lu-jah, praise Jehovah, Amen,

Ev-'ry-bod-y said, A - - - men, Ev-'ry-bod-y said,

lu-jah, praise Jehovah, Amen, A - men, A - men. Ev-'ry-bod-y said,
A - - - men, A - - - men.

Hum ... *Hum* ... *Hum*

1. The Lord is my Shepherd, He leads me day by day: He feeds me
2. John on the Isle of Patmos, Looked over in the Glory Land; He heard the
3. I would not be a de-ceiv-er, I'll tell you the reason why: I'm a-fraid my
4. When I was a sin-ner, A sin-ner just like you, I came to the
5. Sometimes my way is cloud-ed, My path-way all con-fused; I set my

Hum ... *Hum* ... *Hum*

D. C. al Fine

when I'm hun - gry, And hears me when I pray. Ev-'ry-bod-y said,
an - gels sing-ing, And shouting Hal-le-lu-jah! A-men. Ev-'ry-bod-y said,
Lord might call me, And I wouldn't be read-y to die. Ev-'ry-bod-y said,
Lord in re-pent-ance, I be-lieved till I came thru. Ev-'ry-bod-y said,
face tow'rd heav-en, De - ter - mined to go thru. Ev-'ry-bod-y said,

DOWN BY THE RIVER-SIDE

(Ain't A-goin' to Study War No More)

1. Goin' to lay down my bur - den, Down by the riv-er-side, Down by the
2. Goin' to lay down my sword and shield, Down by the riv-er-side, Down by the
3. Goin' to try on my star-ry crown, Down by the riv-er-side, Down by the

riv-er-side, Down by the riv-er-side; Goin' to lay down my bur - den,
riv-er-side, Down by the riv-er-side; Goin' to lay down my sword and shield,
riv-er-side, Down by the riv-er-side; Goin' to try on my star-ry crown,

CHORUS

Down by the riv-er-side, Goin' to stud-y war no more. Ain't a-goin' to

stud-y war no more, Ain't a-goin' to stud-y war no more, Ain't a-goin' to

1. stud-y war no more, ... Ain't a-goin' to stud-y war no more.

Ain't a-goin' to study war no more,

105 WERE YOU THERE WHEN THEY CRUCIFIED MY LORD?

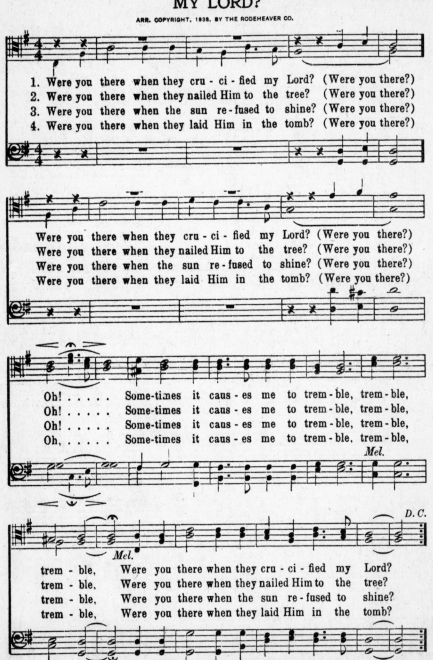

1. Were you there when they cru - ci - fied my Lord? (Were you there?)
2. Were you there when they nailed Him to the tree? (Were you there?)
3. Were you there when the sun re - fused to shine? (Were you there?)
4. Were you there when they laid Him in the tomb? (Were you there?)

Were you there when they cru - ci - fied my Lord? (Were you there?)
Were you there when they nailed Him to the tree? (Were you there?)
Were you there when the sun re - fused to shine? (Were you there?)
Were you there when they laid Him in the tomb? (Were you there?)

Oh! . . . . . Some-times it caus - es me to trem - ble, trem - ble,
Oh! . . . . . Some-times it caus - es me to trem - ble, trem - ble,
Oh! . . . . . Some-times it caus - es me to trem - ble, trem - ble,
Oh, ... Some-times it caus - es me to trem - ble, trem - ble,

Mel.

trem - ble, Were you there when they cru - ci - fied my Lord?
trem - ble, Were you there when they nailed Him to the tree?
trem - ble, Were you there when the sun re - fused to shine?
trem - ble, Were you there when they laid Him in the tomb?

Mel.

D. C.

WERE YOU THERE WHEN THEY CRUCIFIED MY LORD

5. Were you there when He rose up from the dead? (Were you

there?) Were you there when He rose up from the dead?

(Were you there?) Oh! . . . . . Some-times I

feel like shout-in' Glo-ry! Glo-ry! Glo--ry! When I

think how He rose up from the dead! (Were you there?)

Oh, I know the Lord. I know the Lord, I know the Lord laid His

hands on me. Oh, hands on me. Did ev - er you see the
some seek the Lord and
Lord's gone done jes

like be - fore? I know the Lord laid His hands on me; King
don't seek right, I know the Lord laid His hands on me; They
what He said, I know the Lord laid His hands on me; He's

Je - sus preach - in' to the poor!
fool all day and pray all night, I know the Lord laid His
healed the sick and raised the dead,

hands on me. Oh, I know the Lord, I know the Lord,

I KNOW THE LORD LAID HIS HANDS ON ME

I know the Lord laid His hands on me; Oh, I know the Lord,

I know the Lord, I know the Lord laid His hands on me. My hands on me.

Oh,

D. S.

rit.

1 & 2 3

107

GO DOWN, MOSES

ARR. COPYRIGHT, 1926. THE RODEHEAVER CO., OWNER

1. When Is - rael was in E-gypt's land: Let my peo-ple go; Op-
2. Thus saith the Lord, bold Mo - ses said, Let my peo-ple go; If
3. No more shall they in bond-age toil, Let my peo-ple go; Let
4. O let us all from bond-age flee, Let my peo-ple go; And

Mel.

pressed so hard they could not stand, Let my peo-ple go.
not, I'll smite your first-born dead, Let my peo-ple go.
them come out with E-gypt's spoil, Let my peo-ple go.
let us all in Christ be free, Let my peo-ple go.

Go down, Mo-ses,

Mel.

'Way down in E-gypt land, Tell ole Pha-raoh, Let my peo-ple go.

Mel.

Mel.

EZEKIEL SAW DE WHEEL

E - ze-kiel saw de wheel, 'Way up in de mid-dle of de air,

E - ze-kiel saw de wheel, 'Way in de mid-dle of de air.

De big wheel run by faith, And de lit-tle wheel run by de grace of God;

FINE.

'Tis a wheel in a wheel, 'Way in de mid-dle of de air.

1. Oh, some go to church for to sing and shout, 'Way in de mid-dle of de
2. If re-li-gion were a thing that mon-ey could buy, 'Way in de mid-dle of de

D. C.

air, Be - fo' six months dey's all turned out, 'Way in de mid-dle of de air.
air, De rich would live an' de poor would die, 'Way in de mid-dle of de air.

109   I WANT TO GO TO HEAVEN

Oh, I want to go to heav-en when I die, When I die, when I die, Oh, I

FINE

Hum

want to go to heav - en when I die, Ear - ly in the morn - in'.

Hum

1. Oh, brother, will you meet me there some day, There some day, there some day, Oh,
2. Oh, brother, will you meet your mother there, Meet her there, meet her there, Oh,
3. Oh, brother, will you meet your fa-ther there, Meet him there, meet him there, Oh,
4. Oh, brother, will you meet your Saviour there, Meet Him there, meet Him there, Oh,

Hum

D. S.

broth-er, will you meet me there some day, Ear - ly in the morn - in'? Oh, I
broth-er, will you meet your moth-er there, Ear - ly in the morn - in'? Oh, I
broth-er, will you meet your fa - ther there, Ear - ly in the morn - in'? Oh, I
broth-er, will you meet your Sav-iour there, Ear - ly in the morn - in'? Oh, I

1. ꟁ Ma - ry and a - Mar - tha's just gone 'long, ꟁ Ma - ry and a-
2. The preacher and the eld - er's just gone 'long, The preacher and the
3. My fa - ther and my moth-er's just gone 'long, My fa - ther and my

Mar-tha's just gone 'long, ꟁ Ma - ry and a - Mar-tha's just gone 'long, To
eld - er's just gone 'long, The preacher and the eld - er's just gone 'long, To
mother's just gone 'long. My fa - ther and my mother's just gone 'long, To

CHORUS

ring dem charmin' bells. Cryin', Free grace and dying love, Free grace and dying love,

Free grace and dying love, To ring dem charmin' bells; Oh! 'way o-ver Jordan, Lord,

O - ver Jor - dan,

'Way o - ver Jordan, Lord, 'Way o -ver Jordan, Lord, To ring dem charmin' bells.

O - ver Jor - dan, O - ver

GIT ON BOARD, LITTLE CHILLUN

ON MY JOURNEY HOME

Rev. B. H. Hogan

Rev. B. H. Hogan and Laura B. Davis

My Lord, I'm on my jour-ney, My Lord, I'm on my jour-ney, My Lord, I'm on my jour-ney, On my jour-ney home.

FINE Hum

1. I went to the val-ley, I did-n't go to stay, My soul got hap-py and I stayed all day, I got good re-lig-ion and I got it in time, And I'm on my jour-ney home.

2. If you get to heav-en be-fore I do, Just tell my Lord I'm a-com-ing too, For I know His grace will car-ry me thru, And I'm on my jour-ney home.

3. My Lord has done just what He said, He raised the sick and He raised the dead; On the cru-el cross He suf-fered and bled, And I'm on my jour-ney home.

D. S.

4. If re-lig-ion was a thing that money could buy, The rich would live and the poor would die,

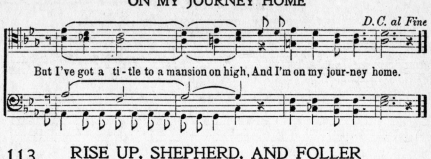

D. C. al Fine

But I've got a ti-tle to a mansion on high, And I'm on my jour-ney home.

113 RISE UP, SHEPHERD, AND FOLLER

Arranged

1. Dere's a Star in de East on Christmas morn; Rise up, shepherd, and fol-ler;
2. Leave yo' sheep, leave yo' sheep, and leave yo' lambs; Rise up, shepherd, and fol-ler;
3. If you take good heed to the an-gel's words; Rise up, shepherd, and fol-ler;

It will lead to de place where de Saviour's born; Rise up, shepherd, and fol-ler.
Leave yo' sheep, leave yo' sheep, leave yo' ewes and lambs; Rise up, shepherd, and fol-ler.
You'll for-get all yo' flocks, you'll forget your herds; Rise up, shepherd, and fol-ler.

CHORUS

Rise up, shep-herd, Rise up, shep-herd, and fol-ler; Oh,

fol-ler the Star of Beth-le-hem, Rise up, shep-herd, and fol-ler.

DEEP RIVER

Deep ... riv-er, My home is o-ver Jor-dan,

Deep ... riv-er, Lord, I want to cross o-ver in-to camp ground.

Oh, don't you want to go .. to de Gos-pel feas'; Dat

prom-ised land where all ... is peace?..

Deep ... riv-er, My home is o-ver Jor-dan,

DEEP RIVER

Deep . . . . riv - er, Lord, I want to cross o - ver in - to camp ground.

Hum

115 LORD, I WANT TO BE A CHRISTIAN

Arr. for this work

1. Lord, I want to be a Chris-tian, In - a my heart, In - a my heart;
2. Lord, I want to be more lov - ing, In - a my heart, In - a my heart;
3. Lord, I want to be like Je - sus, In - a my heart, In - a my heart;

Lord, I want to be a Chris-tian, In - a my heart... In - a my
Lord, I want to be more lov - ing, In - a my heart... In - a my
Lord, I want to be like Je - sus, In - a my heart... In - a my

heart, ... in - a my heart; . . . . . Lord, I want to
In - a my heart, in - a my heart; Lord, I want to
Lord, I want to

be a Chris-tian, In - a my heart. Chris-tian, In - a my heart.
be more lov - ing, In - a my heart. lov - ing, In - a my heart.
be like Je - sus, In - a my heart. Je - sus, In - a my heart.

116 DON'T TOLL ANY BELL FOR ME

A. A. P.

A. A. Payn

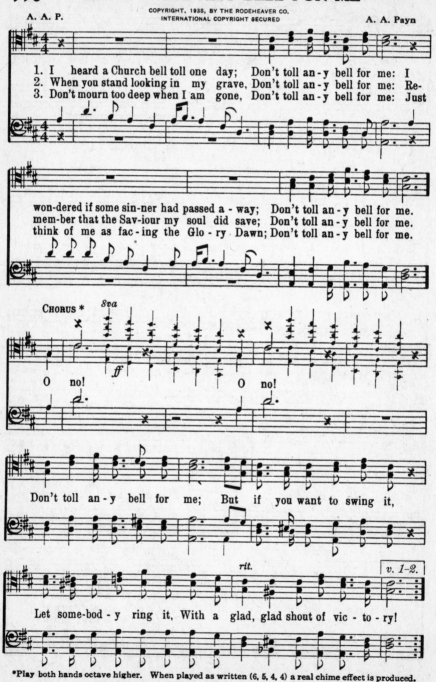

1. I heard a Church bell toll one day; Don't toll an-y bell for me: I
2. When you stand looking in my grave, Don't toll an-y bell for me: Re-
3. Don't mourn too deep when I am gone, Don't toll an-y bell for me: Just

won-dered if some sin-ner had passed a-way; Don't toll any bell for me.
mem-ber that the Sav-iour my soul did save; Don't toll any bell for me.
think of me as fac-ing the Glo-ry Dawn; Don't toll any bell for me.

CHORUS *

O no! O no!

Don't toll an-y bell for me; But if you want to swing it,

rit.

v. 1-2.

Let some-bod-y ring it, With a glad, glad shout of vic-to-ry!

*Play both hands octave higher. When played as written (6, 5, 4, 4) a real chime effect is produced.

DON'T TOLL ANY BELL FOR ME

LITTLE DAVID

117

Lit - tle Da - vid, play on your harp, Hal - le - lu! Hal - le -
lu! Lit - tle Da - vid, play on your harp, Hal - le - lu! Lit - tle Da - vid,

harp, Hal - le - lu!

1. Lit - tle Da - vid was a shep-herd boy, He
2. Oh, Josh - ua was the son of Nun, He
3. Done tole you once, done tole you twice, Dere's

killed Go - li - ath, an' he shout - ed for joy.
nev - er would stop till the work was done. Lit - tle Da - vid,
sin - ners in hell for shoot - in' dice.

NO HIDIN' PLACE

Dere's no hid-in' place down dere, Dere's no hid-in' place down dere, I went to de rock to hide my face, De rock cried out, "No hid-in' place, No hid-in' place down here." Ah, ...

Oh, de rock cried, "I'm burn-in' Burn-in' too! Ah, ... Help me, Lawd! too!". . . . Oh, de rock cried, "I'm burn-in' too!". . . .

NO HIDIN' PLACE

NO HIDIN' PLACE

NO HIDIN' PLACE

STEAL AWAY

Steal a - way, Steal a - way, Steal a-way to Je - sus! Steal a - way,

Steal a - way home, I ain't got long to stay here. Steal a - way,

Steal a-way, Steal a-way to Je - sus! *Hum* *Hum*..........

Steal a-way, steal a-way home, I

Hum................ {My Lord calls me, He calls me by the / Green trees are bend-ing, Poor sin-ners are a-

ain't got long to stay here.

D. C. al Fine

thun - der; The trumpet sounds with-in-a my soul! I ain't got long to stay here.
trembling; The trumpet sounds with-in-a my soul! I ain't got long to stay here.

120 WHEN THE WORLD'S ON FIRE

MUSIC COPYRIGHT, 1928   WORDS COPYRIGHT, 1934
THE RODEHEAVER CO., OWNER
INTERNATIONAL COPYRIGHT SECURED

A. A. Payn   Spiritual

1. Day of judg-ment may be near-ing—What a morn-ing that will be!
2. When the dawn-ing of that morn-ing Breaks in fu-ry o'er the world;
3. Sin-ners trembling, saints re-joic-ing, Each de-part-ing to His place;

There'll be safe-ty then in Je-sus,—"Rock of A-ges, cleft for me."
Rocks and mountains, streams and fountains, In con-fu-sion will be hurled.
All the ran-somed Christ will gath-er, He has saved them by His grace.

CHORUS

1-2. O my lov-ing broth-er, when the world's on fi-re
3. O my poor mourn-er, when the world's on fi-re

Don't you want God's bos-om to be your pil-low? Hide me

o-ver in the Rock of A-ges, Rock of A-ges, cleft for me.

SWING LOW, SWEET CHARIOT

Arrangement Copyright, 1938, by The Rodeheaver Co.

SWING LOW, SWEET CHARIOT

SWING LOW, SWEET CHARIOT

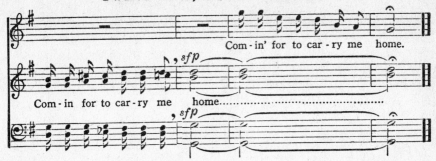

122 CARRY ME BACK TO OLD VIRGINNY

Arrangement Copyright, 1938, by The Rodeheaver Co.

CARRY ME BACK TO OLD VIRGINNY

CARRY ME BACK TO OLD VIRGINNY

123 AMERICA FOR ME

WORDS COPYRIGHT, 1909. MUSIC COPYRIGHT, 1914, RENEWAL 1942
THE RODEHEAVER CO., OWNER
INTERNATIONAL COPYRIGHT SECURED

Dr. Henry Van Dyke

C. Austin Miles

1. 'Tis fine to see the Old World, and trav-el up and down
2. O Lon-don is a man's town, there's pow-er in the air;
3. I know that Eu-rope's won-der-ful, yet some-thing seems to lack;

A-mong the fa-mous pal-a-ces and cit-ies of re-nown,
And Par-is is a wo-man's town, with flow-ers in her hair;
The Past is too much with her, and the peo-ple look-ing back;

To ad-mire the crum-bly cas-tles and the stat-ues of the kings,
And it's sweet to dream in Ven-ice, and it's great to stud-y Rome;
But the glo-ry of the Pres-ent is to make the Fu-ture free,

But now I think I've had e-nough of an-ti-quat-ed things.
But when it comes to liv-ing, there is no place like home.
We love our land for what she is, and what she is to be.

REFRAIN

So its home a-gain, and home a-gain, A-mer-i-ca for me,

AMERICA FOR ME

My heart is turn-ing home a-gain, and there I long to be,

Last Refrain
I want a ship that's west-ward bound, to plow the roll-ing sea,

In the land of youth and free-dom, be-yond the o-cean bars,
To the bless-ed land of Room-enough, be-yond the o-cean bars,

Where the air is full of sun-light, And the flag is full of stars.

124 DREAM OF MY HEART

A. H. A.   A. H. ACKLEY

I'm liv-ing in dreams that I hope will come true, When love builds a

pal-ace for me, A home in an old-fash-ioned gar-den for two, or

DREAM OF MY HEART

DREAM OF MY HEART

breez - es are blow - ing, A pal - ace di - vine that shall

some-day be mine, Is the won - der - ful dream of my heart.

125 SANTA LUCIA

Neapolitan Boat Song

1. Now 'neath the sil - ver moon o - cean is glow - ing, O'er the calm bil - low
   Here balm - y breez-es blow, pure joys in - vite us, And as we gent-ly row,

CHORUS

Soft winds are blowing. Hark! how the sail-ors cry, Joy - ous - ly e-choes nigh
All things de-light us. Home of fair po-e - sy, Realm of pure har-mo - ny,

1.
2.

San - ta Lu - ci - a, San - ta Lu - ci - a, San - ta Lu - ci - a.

126 DRINK TO ME ONLY WITH THINE EYES

BEN JOHNSON

Old English Air
Arr. N. P.

1. Drink to me on-ly with thine eyes, And I will pledge with
2. I sent thee late a ros-y wreath, Not so much hon-'ring

mine; Or leave a kiss with-in the cup, And
thee As giv-ing it a hope that there It

I'll not ask for wine; The thirst that from the
would not with-ered be; But thou there-on didst

soul doth rise, Doth ask a drink di-vine; But might I
on-ly breathe, And send'st it back to me, Since when it

of Jove's nec-tar sip, I would not change for thine.
grows and smells, I swear, Not of it's self but thee.

1. Soft o'er the foun - tain ling-'ring falls the south-ern moon, Far o'er the
2. When in thy dream-ing moons like these shall shine a-gain, And day-light

moun-tain breaks the day too soon; In thy dark eyes splen-dor, where the
beam-ing prove thy dreams are vain; Wilt thou not re - lent - ing, for thine

warm light loves to dwell, Wea - ry looks yet ten - der, speak their fond
ab - sent lov - er sigh, In thy heart con - sent-ing to a prayer

fare - well. Ni - ta, Jua - ni - ta, ask thy soul if we should part.
gone by. Ni - ta, Jua - ni - ta, let me ling - er by thy side.

should part

Ni - ta, Jua - ni - ta, lean thou on my heart.
Ni - ta, Jua - ni - ta, be my own fair bride.

Come where my love lies dream - ing, Dream-ing the happy hours a - way;

In vis - ions bright re - deem - ing, The fleet-ing joys of day;

Hum
Dream-ing the hap-py hours, Dream-ing the hap-py hours a - way;............
Hum

My own love is sweet - ly
Come where my love lies dream-ing, Dream - ing the
p

My own love is sweet-ly
hap - py hours a - way, Come where my love lies dream - ing..................

COME WHERE MY LOVE LIES DREAMING

COME WHERE MY LOVE LIES DREAMING

MEDLEY OF NURSERY RHYMES

Arr. by NORMAN PRICE

When Mother comes into my room, to tuck me in - to bed, She brings my book of

nurs'ry rhymes, cov-ered all in red, And reads to me the ones I like, and

MEDLEY OF NURSERY RHYMES

some I nev-er heard, With now and then a tune thrown in a-bout a flow'r or bird;

Be-fore she sings my lul-la-by and I be-gin to doze, My dad-dy comes a-

long and tries to pinch me on the nose. Ah! would you like my twi-light hour, so

MEDLEY OF NURSERY RHYMES

come a-long and see my dad and mother by my bed, and hear them sing to me.

Ma - ry had a lit - tle lamb, lit - tle lamb, lit - tle lamb,
Ev - 'ry-where that Ma - ry went, Ma - ry went, Ma - ry went,

Ma - ry had a lit - tle lamb. Its fleece was white as snow,
Ev - 'ry-where that Ma - ry went The lamb was sure to go.

MEDLEY OF NURSERY RHYMES

MEDLEY OF NURSERY RHYMES

MEDLEY OF NURSERY RHYMES

She was a dain - ty rose-bud, Far too grand for him,

He was a lit - tle tin sol-dier, One lit-tle leg had he,

Brave-ly he shouldered his mus - ket, Fain her love would be; Lul-la -

MEDLEY OF NURSERY RHYMES

by and good-night, thy moth-er's de-light, Bright an-gels a-

round my dar-ling shall stand; Go to sleep, close thine eyes, Thou shalt

see Par-a-dise, Thou shalt wake when God will from thy slumber so still.

130 I JEST KEEP A-LIVIN' A-LONG

FRANK L. STANTON

HOMER RODEHEAVER

Hum

1. Some folks they keep hunt-in' for sor-row;............They
2. When the Lord made the world was I in it................. To
3. I'm......... thank-ful for sun and for show-ers;............. The

sigh if they're right or they're wrong......... But this day's as
give him di-rec-tions? He knowed........ I would-n't know
Lord makes the win-ter and May;........ He'd hide all the

good as to-mor-row,......... So I jest keep a liv-in' a-long.
how to be-gin it,............ Bein' noth-in' but dust by the road.
graves with his flow-ers,........... If folks did not weed them a-way.

CHORUS

I jest keep a liv-in' a-long.................. I just keep a
I jest keep a liv-in' a-long..................And I can't say the
I jest keep a liv-in' a-long ....Still thank-ful for the

Liv-in' a long

I JEST KEEP A-LIVIN' A-LONG

sing - in' a song.............. There's no use to sigh while the
Lord's work is wrong.............. I nev - er will sigh while He's
sun - light and song;.............. I know when it's blow-in', God's

Sing - in' a song
Lord's work is wrong
Sun - light and song

sun's in the sky; So I jest keep a - liv - in' a - long............
run - nin' the sky; So I jest keep a - liv - in' a - long............
ros - es are blow - in; So I jest keep a - liv - in' a - long............

Liv - in' a - long.

131 ## POP! GOES THE WEASEL

Copyright, 1931, The Rodeheaver Co., owner

G. W. Payne v. 2 and 3   International Copyright Secured

1. All a-round the cob-bler's bench The mon-key chased the wea-sel; The
2. The wea - sel grabs the mon-key's tail, The mon-key grabs the oth - er's, And
3. The mon - key climbs the chan-de-lier And looks down on the wea - sel. Turns

*   REFRAIN

mon-key tho't 'twas all in fun, Pop! Goes the wea-sel!
round and round the room they sail Just like twin brothers. } I've no time to wait or sigh, No
on the gas and, Dear! O Dear! Pop goes the wea-sel.

patience to wait till by and by; Kiss me quick, I'm off, good-bye, Pop! Goes the weasel.

NOTE, – Original meaning of "pop" is to pawn; weasel is a "flat-iron." *May be sung by single voice.

CARRY ON!

ROBERT SERVICE*   HOMER RODEHEAVER

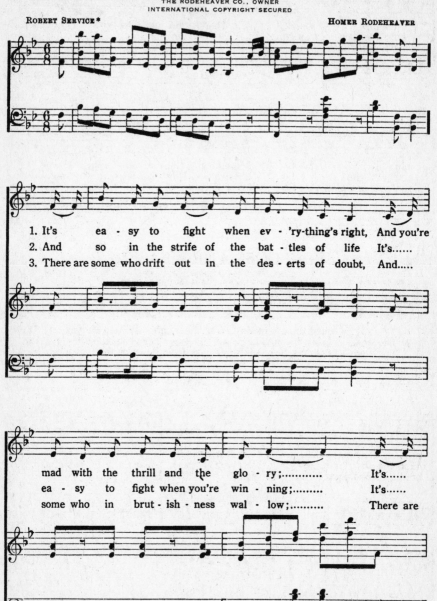

1. It's   ea - sy to   fight   when ev - 'ry-thing's right, And you're
2. And   so   in the strife of   the bat - tles of   life   It's......
3. There are some who drift   out   in   the des - erts of doubt,   And.....

mad with   the   thrill and the   glo - ry;............   It's......
ea - sy   to   fight when you're   win - ning;.........   It's......
some who   in   brut - ish - ness   wal - low;..........   There are

* From " Rhymes of a Red Cross Man." By Robert W. Service

Published by Barse & Hopkins, New York City

CARRY ON!

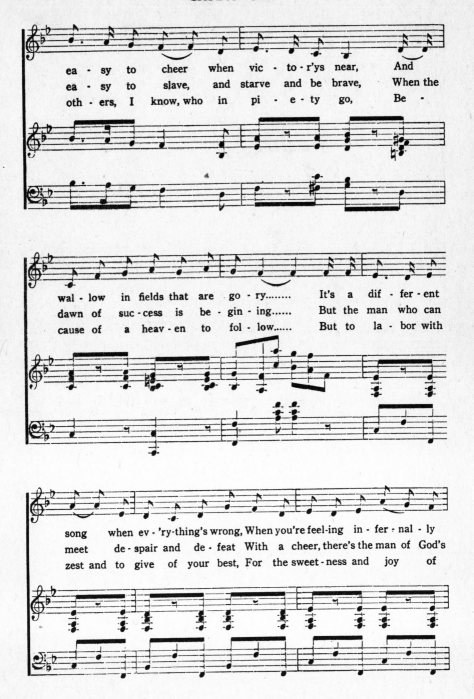

CARRY ON!

CARRY ON!

ALL ON DECK

Arr. by Norman Price

ALL ON DECK

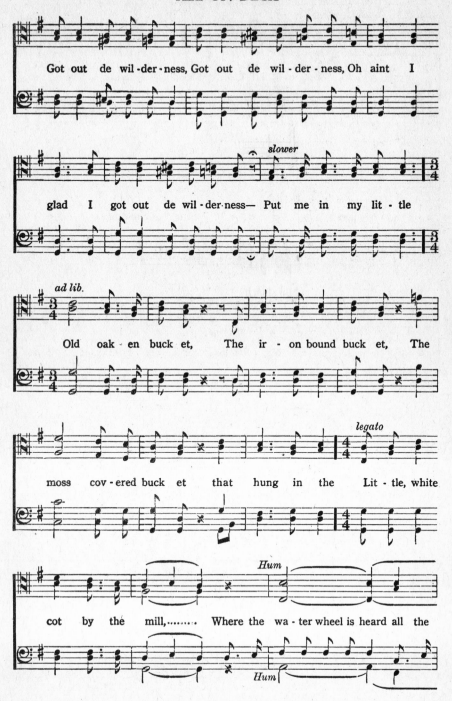

Got out de wil-der-ness, Got out de wil-der-ness, Oh aint I

glad I got out de wil-der-ness— Put me in my lit-tle

Old oak-en buck-et, The ir-on bound buck-et, The

moss cov-ered buck-et that hung in the Lit-tle, white

cot by the mill,........ Where the wa-ter wheel is heard all the

ALL ON DECK

day,.......... Back to child-hood my thoughts will re-turn, re-turn,

Tho' my home may be far. I hear the chil-dren call-ing, I

see their sad tears fall-ing, My heart turns back to Dix-ie, and

We must Hail Co-lum-bia, hap-py land, Yan-kee Doo-dle hand in hand,

Three cheers for the Red, White and Blue, Three cheers for the Red, White and

ALL ON DECK

Blue-beard was a sol-dier, His hair was jet-white black, He dressed in reg - i -
men-tals, With a knap-sack on his Yan-kee Doo-dle came to town, A-
rid-ing on a po - ny. He stuck a feath-er in his cap and
called him mac - a - - ro - ni. Come with me, come with me, come
come with me, To my home, to my home, Down by the sea.

ALL ON DECK

Call all hands to man the cap-stan, See the ca-ble runs all clear,

And a-cross the bri-ny o-cean, we, our gal-lant bark shall steer.

Roll-in' home, Roll-in' home, Roll-in' home a-cross the sea, Roll-in'

home a-cross the o-cean, Roll-in' home dear land to thee. We'll

call all hands on the deck. We'll call all hands on the deck. Row, brothers, row.

TOPICAL INDEX

159

INDEX